The Official Book of Running

The Official Book of Running

by Bill Emmerton

World Authority Ultra-Long Distance Runner

with Cliff Gewecke

*The Experts Guide for
Beginner Jogger to Advanced Runner*

BOOK CRAFT GUILD, INC.
NEW YORK, NEW YORK

To all the wonderful people I have been so fortunate to meet and get to know throughout my travels.

To many good friends who have helped me.

To all the joggers and runners in the world I feel so close to.

Contents

Introduction

Australian - born Bill Emmerton has run more than 130,000 documented miles in the past 38 years - more than any other man in the world. He has been hailed by *Readers Digest* as "The Runningest Bloke Alive", dubbed by Billy Graham as "The Evangelist Of Physical Fitness" and has been accorded high honors and recognition from governmental and medical people throughout the world.

These titles have been well earned, as can be amazed at in the listing covering many of Bill's seemingly impossible feats. His achievements have been widely publicized in newspaper features throughout the world, and in magazine articles in *Sports Illustrated, Life, Time, Newsweek,* and many other publications. In addition, he has been interviewed extensively on radio and television panel-talk-shows throughout the country.

Apart from his running career, Emmerton is also a well known author and lecturer. Bill's personal crusade has taken him around the world (four times) and throughout the U.S. lecturing at universities and before medical groups on the benefits of physical fitness and proper nutrition. He is a Board Member of the National Jogging Association; on the President's Council of Physical Fitness; Member of the American Medical Jogging Association and a Chief Lecturer of the U.S. Y.M.C.A. Organization.

"The Official Book Of Running" represents the gathering of Bill Emmerton's lifetime of knowledge, experience and insight into the world of running and fitness, for all ages and stages of experience.

BILL EMMERTON

"THE RUNNINGEST BLOKE ALIVE"

MARATHON RECORDS:

1978   THE ORIGINAL PONY EXPRESS RUN. A record 2,000 mile run through parts of eight states (Missouri, Kansas, Nebraska, Colorado, Wyoming, Utah, Nevada, California). Emmerton accomplished this grueling run over some of the world's most difficult terrain. Starting on May 2nd, he finished on June 20, 1978; a total of 50 days of continuous running, averaging over 40 miles a day. He is the first person ever to cover the full length of the route on foot.

1975   Death Valley match race with Bobby Riggs - Riggs ran 25 miles in 8 hours, 10 minutes. Emmerton ran 50 miles in 8 hours, 40 minutes. See *Time, Newsweek, Sports Illustrated* magazines -January 5 editions (1976)

1974   Across the Grand Canyon from South rim to top of the North rim - 22 miles in 7 hours - One of the shortest, yet most agonizing of his endurance feats.

1973   From South rim of Grand Canyon - 21 miles in 4 hours, 30 minutes, continued for 14 more miles. Previous record: 5 hours, 42 minutes.

1972   Record walk through Death Valley from Shoshone to Scotty's Castle, California - 130 miles in 4 days, 15 hours, 51 minutes - in temperatures ranging to 126 degrees.

1969   From Houston to Cape Kennedy, Florida - 1100 miles in 27 consecutive days - To pay honor to the first U.S. moon launching. Following a 3 day examination by NASA physicians at Houston, they reported: "The most striking of our findings is Mr. Emmerton's superb performance in the exercise response test...His exercise capacity is as good as that of the best response we have observed in any of our astronaunt population."

1968   Two runs: First: Through Death Valley - 130 miles in 3 days, in 126 degrees heat. Second: Continuing on to Las Vegas - 211 miles in 3 days, 15 hours, 40 minutes. A blistering ground temperature of 134 degrees was recorded.

1967   From Toronto to Montreal - 390 miles in 7 days - A salute to the opening of the Expo '67.

1965   From New York to Washington, D.C. - 254 miles in 5 days - A tribute to the late President John F. Kennedy's Physical Fitness program.

1965   From John O'Groats, Scotland to Land's End, England - 954 miles in 18 days, 10 hours. The longest run ever made in the British Empire.

1965   From Melbourne to Adelaide, Australia - 500 miles in 10 days.

1963   From Edinborough to Glasgow, Scotland - 48 miles in 5 hours, 45 minutes.

1963   153 miles non-stop in 29 hours.

1962   168 miles non-stop in 32 hours, 35 minutes.

1

WHY RUN?

What It Can Do For You

Old Ponce de Leon roamed the world in search of the "Fountain of Youth," never quite finding it.

Now, if old Ponce had just RUN around the world—or even in his own neighborhood, for that matter—then he might well have uttered the famous cry (as did the California goldminer) of "Eureka"—I have found it!

I always smile when I hear the famous story about Ponce de Leon. And I'm reminded by it of a study of the London busdrivers and their conductors, taken some years ago.

The drivers, with the "best" job of just sitting all day and driving their buses, did not live for the most part as long as the conductors—who all day were hopping up and down, in and out, of the buses. They were, of course, literally jogging, working the heart and muscles, keeping fit. The drivers got little such exercise.

The point of it all is that the "Fountain of Youth" is not some spray of water that you can stand under—or drink— that will wash away the years, giving eternal youth.

No, that magic fountain is an internal matter—a "wash- from-within," that comes from hard work and plenty of ac- tivity.

When you run—long enough, fast enough, yes hard enough—you will perspire, "washing from within," cleans- ing the toxins from your system, oxidizing the blood, and that is the so-called "Fountain of Youth", or the closest we can come to it.

There is a great deal of research indicating that by run- ning regularly, a person can add some years and certainly "feeling-better-years" to his life, and I'm not going to dis- pute it. But neither am I going to claim "my sport" as the cure-all. All I'm suggesting is that you look into it's potential benefits "FOR YOU".

I know that I have had very few sick days in the 40 years that I've been running, that I have the pep of many men 20 years my junior, and that most people I meet say that I look 10 to 15 years younger than I am.

MEDICAL OPINION

A California friend of mine, the pathologist, Dr. Tom Bassler, claims that he has never known of anybody who completed a marathon who died of a heart attack. He theo- rizes that one's life expectancy is proportional to the distance he, (or she), can cover on foot. Ultra-marathons, therefore; seem to be the answer to longevity. Tom, and his friends and family, are into "jogs" of 50 miles, more or less.

If there's anyone who should agree with Dr. Bassler, of course, it's me. For years I've been running ultra-ultra- marathons, (from city to city), in both Australia and the United States.

Most everyone, I'm sure, is aware of the pronouncements of Dr. Paul Dudley White, former President Eisenhower's physician, about the value—indeed necessity—of vigorous exercise for health. Other doctors have since said much the same. A growing number of them have turned to jogging—or running—for their "vigorous exercise."

The heart is actually a muscle, and I don't think there's much doubt that you can strengthen it (as well as other muscles) and thereby help in the pumping of blood throughout the body, by an exercise like running. A great many medical sources will tell you this. I suggest that you investigate further.

Some medical men, on the other hand, have questioned running, or jogging, saying its benefits aren't always what they are claimed. And they cite dangers: such as heart attacks brought on by over-exertion, or other possible injuries due to the pounding of one's feet onto the ground.

As in any controversy, there are always some who question the specific benefits from a course of action. In any event, I definitely believe that before anyone gets out and starts running, they should have an examination by a qualified physician. If the doctor says, no, jogging isn't for you— then take his advise. Health, running, is an extremely individual matter.

I also believe that once you start jogging you should do it by degrees. There's an old adage: "Inch by inch it's a cinch: yard by yard it's so hard." If you are pronounced fit to run by your doctor, then don't go out immediately and try to run the four-minute mile. In the first place you won't. And in the second, if you work up by degrees, you'll surpass all sorts of barriers with hardly any difficultly. In a later chapter, we'll get into programs for both the beginner and the more advanced runner.

CAMARADERIE

But even if running can't guarantee that you will live to be 100, it has so much to offer. In the first place, it's about as inexpensive an activity as there is. You can, of course, buy all sorts of fancy shoes, warmup suit, stop-watch, shorts, jersey, etc., and if you get into jogging seriously you probably will. But all you really need (except for the basic clothing) is time and space, indoors and outdoors, for running either in place or the moving-ahead kind.

I have found jogging, also, to be an exceedingly democratic sport. There is little, if any, discrimination based on profession, class, sex, race, anything. Enter a race and the man next to you at the starting line might be a corporation president. Jog in the park and you might pass a movie star, or the local supermarket manager.

It, indeed, is a beautiful way to make friends, because you are sharing a common bond of effort, if you run hard and fast enough.

One of the reasons Arthur Lydiard, an Olympic team coach from New Zealand, created the idea for those long, slow runs—that, really, initiated the jogging boom—was because many of his former competitors missed the camaraderie of their sport.

FITNESS

Many people, myself included, haven't the time, or the skill to play some of the other sports. Especially sports that are going to be of any real physical-fitness benefit.

And so, the answer is simple: running. It requires no great skill to enjoy it and your level of competitive fitness is a direct result of the mileage and effort you put into it. The only real "skill" is foot-speed, and that is only necessary if you're going to race. Some races—like the ultra-ultra-marathons—don't even require speed . . . just lasting power at a slow pace.

But let's say you do have a favorite sport: like tennis, golf, racquetball, softball, whatever; that is played on dry land, (or floors), where better foot movement is a decided advantage.

I certainly would not say that running will automatically make you a better tennis player, for example; because there are a lot of stroke skills, tactics, strategy and the ability to know where and when to move to meet the travelling ball. I know a lot of older (or, yes, young) players who can beat the pants off less-experienced, so-called "more fit" persons.

But some studies have indicated that many of these skilled players aren't REALLY fit. They just seem fit. They have played for many years with an ability to get the maximum results out of the minimum movement. And in many of these sports, the movements are, in reality, short bursts that give little exercise to the heart. This, again, is in direct contrast to our friend Tom Bassler's long-slow-continuous-movement-gives-longevity-concept. Think about it! Investigate and seek out your own answers.

My belief if that the person seeking total usage of his life-style abilities—be they sport-related, job-related, or personal-related—should have fitness as the basic tool. What about when two older tennis players, who know all the right moves, play against each other? Doesn't it figure that as the match wears on and condition becomes a factor (maybe the key) that the jogger wins out over the non-jogger.

I know that before running became "stylish," and very few other athletes were running, Rod Laver—the Australian tennis player—WAS, something like six miles every day. At his peak (during the 1960s) he was the kingpin, and I believe he won many games, sets, matches, on the stamina gained during those jogs. Now, of course, great numbers of the top pro (and amateur) athletes run to improve their playing abilities.

Oddly enough, besides its other virtues, maybe the greatest "daily living" virtue of running, is the discipline it gives in matters of critical importance; like eating, sleeping, and thinking. And a lot of people swear it has improved their sex life tremendously. What more could you ask?

EATING

Everyone knows that your weight—given a certain body structure—is for the most part directly a result of the number of calories you take in. There are exceptions, of course, of people who just "burn up" or can't handle an abundance of calories and of those who have an organic illness that leads to over (or under) weight.

But for most of us, we definitely are what we eat: fat, slender, trim, husky, whatever. And even if we seem to do plenty of exercise, it doesn't mean we'll take off those pounds, if we are also eating a lot. It is, really, a vicious cycle.

As a result, all sorts of diets offering all kinds of "magical" ways to cut down on food consumption are now available—some pretty good, some obviously terrible. They run the gamut: from simple near starvation to interesting mixtures of the low-calorie foods, to the so called "miracle" pills and fad diets.

In a later chapter, we'll discuss food and diet, with a sensible, healthful approach. And one that cooperates with your program of running, whether you are a beginner jogger or an experienced long-distance runner.

Eating to run (and vice versa) is very important, because one of the interesting side-effects, or disciplines, of running is that the body usually goes through changes and actually craves less food. It also seems to direct itself toward the more-nourishing, non-junk food. At one and the same time, the body seems to be saying: I don't want a lot of food because my running nourishes me, (via breathing, blood circulation, perspiration), as well as tires me, but whatever I do need has to be quality food.

Now you know why most longer-distance runners are slender, and none that I know are "fat." They'd rather run than eat! Put another way, they eat so they can run, not run, in order to eat. I'm sure they enjoy food and drink, but eating beyond their body's needs becomes a "secondary" pleasure.

DRINKING AND SMOKING

Speaking of disciplines, one of the biggest that running offers is against those twin "killers"—excessive drinking and smoking. The longer (and more often) you run, the less you crave either. It's as if the body is saying: I'm "nourished" naturally, I don't need this. The same could be said for some of the drugs that some people take. Indeed, REAL runners can't afford to smoke or drink or "drug" because it curtails their efficiency as well as "good feelings" during and even after a jog.

I want to make it clear to you that I'm not against taking an occasional drink socially. I drink occasionally myself— mostly, beer, I might add, which tends to be the runners' favorite beverage. Some even drink it during a long marathon—and certainly afterwards.

TENSION

One of the reasons people smoke, drink, even eat (or a variety of other things), is simply to relieve tension. Both physical and a mind-type (psychological) tension, brought on by job, family, and all sorts of personal problems. And you'd be surprised how easily and quickly a jog around the block (or the park), can help relieve this uptightness.

When you are running, you are absorbed, relaxed mentally, able to think more clearly, not worrying about anything, really, except continuing with the next step ahead. When you finish, a pleasant fatigue, coupled with accomplishment, takes hold, and this can keep away tension for quite some time.

And even when you are not tense, a daily jog prepares you for the possibility of rough times. The divorce from my first wife was a very trying period for me. But I was able to deal with it, I believe, because of my running, which always seemed to put life back into proper perspective.

CREATIVITY

Talk to most runners and they'll tell you that the time they do some of their clearest thinking, ridding the mind of unnecessary clutter, is during a run. The brain is stimulated during a run—able to focus almost brilliantly at times. My friend, Erich Segal, has said he wrote the first chapter of "Love Story" during the course of his running. Others create songs, new ideas, better approaches to their job, what have you. So the criticism that jogging is "boring" compared to more play-oriented sports doesn't hold true. It can be totally productive if you are a thinking person.

SLEEP

A good night's sleep can be a problem for some people. I haven't had that problem—not since I started running many years ago. There is something about running that fatigues, yet pacifies the body so that it can be ready for sound sleep ... consistently.

In order to have sufficient energy for their morning or evening run, many people find that they must discipline (there's that word again) themselves to be in bed, say by 10 or 11 o'clock. But, also, many have discovered that after a while, they actually need fewer hours of sleep to maintain the same vitality they had previously. A fit, healthy body is able to withstand more-than-usual stress; the fact that you need less sleep is a good sign.

SEX

What to do with the extra hours you now have because you need fewer hours of sleep? How about an improved sex life—and once again our good friend running is a multi-faceted worker. Men, especially, want to perform up to certain ideals (presumably), so endurance is a key factor. You get endurance via running! You also get a more virile self-image, as well as a fit appearance that can make you more attractive looking.

For women, of course, jogging can help the figure, as well as endurance and self-image, the same as for the men. And, I'm told, women joggers (especially those whose husbands also run), usually have fewer headaches.

Many studies I've read, indicate that women maintain an interest in sex (and capacity for it) longer years than do many men. But this, in my opinion, needn't be. I have plenty of friends in their 50s, 60s and 70s (all runners, of course), who enjoy a very active sex life. Indeed, the studies show that a man's ability is not measured by his chronological years so much as by his state of fitness for those years! And that fitness (sexually) is restorable between ages 40 to 60 by exercise. So get it together, men!

AESTHETICS

By now, I'm sure you're thinking there can't be any better reasons to run that top the joy of a better sex life. But as I wind down this chapter, I'd like to mention one other reason: the pure beauty of it all!

When you are running, and fit, there's a certain almost inexplicable closeness to and caring for your body that you become aware of. A kind of rhythm beats from within that by the same token is in tune with the surrounding world.

If you're fortunate enough to have run (or make a point of doing it regularly) in surroundings of great natural beauty, it can almost be a poetic experience. I know, I've had the experience many times in my runs across country on three continents.

Roger Bannister, in his book "First Four Minutes," tells about a childhood experience, seeing the clouds above, the sand at his feet as he stood barefoot near the sea.

"In this supreme moment I leapt in sheer joy," he wrote. "I was startled, and frightened, by the tremendous excitement that so few steps could create . . . The earth seemed almost to move with me. I was running now, and a fresh rhythm entered my body. No longer conscious of my movement, I discovered a new unity with nature. I had found a new source of power and beauty, a source I never dreamt existed."

Well said, obviously, from a man who made running history. And you too, can experience similar feelings. Try it (if you already haven't), it will open up a new world for you.

2

WHO RUNS?

A Sport For All Ages

All over the world, people are taking up the "new" sport, Jogging and Running.

In California, there's a grandmother in her late 80s who runs a mile or so nearly every day. She won gold medals in a recent Senior Olympics and, I'm told, holds the "world record" for a mile in her age category.

Who cares, you ask?

You, for one, should . . . unless you're out there trying to stay fit like our running grandmother, Eula Weaver, is.

In my mind her tenacity at an advanced age ranks right up there with Roger Bannister's 1954 accomplishment of being the first in history to run the four-minute mile. Roger was in his 20s at the time.

But even Eula may have to take a back seat to a gentlemen I met several years ago named Larry Lewis. You probably know of him as the "jogging waiter" from San Francisco, who every morning for years ran his six miles in Golden Gate Park. At age 103 he "sprinted" 100 yards in 17 seconds—truly remarkable—and until near his death at 106 he continued his job at the hotel and his running.

Not many of us, of course, are going to live to Lewis' ripe old age—even if we run six miles a day. But starting Now— your chances of reaching Lewis' (or Eula Weaver's) golden age will have improved, according to observations by many doctors.

You could, depending on your foot speed, your drive, your conditioning, even break new barriers that latter-day authors will write about. One sure thing about running is that there is no absolute. Records are made to be broken. Besides which, breaking barriers, setting time standards, is only the tip of the iceberg . . . something writers can't resist mentioning.

The bottom line is, simply, that you'll feel vastly better, look much better, feel more alive for all the years of your life. That, in my mind, is worth all the time, effort, pain, whatever you choose to devote to your running.

STARTING

For years, I've felt that the younger you can start running the better. I personally took up the sport at age 17 because of poor health, in Tasmaina, my home state in Australia. A doctor advised me to curtail exercise, but instead I started a program of running.

When I visited this same doctor several months later he was amazed at the progress of my health. He couldn't believe that just plain running had worked such a miracle. But I knew, and I've never stopped since.

I only wish, now, that I'd started running sooner. Most children like to run. It's a natural, free-spirited thing . . . a play activity. Once the child gets out of the crawling, into the walking stage, he just WANTS to express himself by running. It's only as we grow older, into our teens, into adulthood, that we begin to curtail our "running".

That, in my opinion, is the start of unfitness. Many persons, tragically, grow too old too soon simply because they assumed that running was something that only athletes did.

I say that's wrong. Run to the store. Run home from work. Run in the park at the company picnic. Run, run, run and never stop—not any day that you can possibly do it. You'll never regret it.

Having lived in the United States now for the past decade or so, I've watched the growing trend toward organized running programs for ALL ages, and sexes. There is a cruel irony to the statement made by Helsinki detective Eino Oksanen, twice winner of the Boston Marathon, who remarked, "In Finland, we don't ride around in automobiles like you do over here. There, everybody runs."

MARATHONS

According to the latest Gallup Poll, there are now some "twenty-three" million Americans—men, women, and children—who jog and run in one fashion or another. The famed Boston Marathon, which had about 600 entrants in the late 1960's, now has thousands of runners, all hoping to finish the testing 26 miles, 385 yards.

Boston isn't the only marathon—they are flourishing all over these days—but so far no other race catches the "pulse" of the running movement quite the same.

For years it attracted a hard-core of veteran entrants who'd grind their way through the city's streets to the interest of onlookers. Any man could enter, but only a special few did.

It had its "Mr. Marathoner," Clarence DeMar, a seven-time winner, who competed until the year before his death at 70; and John A. Kelley, who ran every year, with one exception; plus many others from all over the world.

But there were no women (they weren't allowed) nor youngsters. Then in 1966 Roberta Gibb Hingay, who'd trained for long distances and whose husband was running, sprang out of the bushes near the starting line after the main group of runners had passed and ran the distance, completing it in 3 hours, 21 minutes and 2 seconds—124th in an all-male field of 416.

Because women were not allowed in the race, Roberta's achievement wasn't recognized by the Boston Athletic Association—though news of it certainly did not go unnoticed by others. The next year, in fact, a "K. Switzer" officially entered and was accepted. Officials did not check out the fact that this, indeed, was Kathy Switzer, who showed up race day "hidden" in a hooded sweatshirt and after a scuffle with an official at the start, finished the race in about four and one-half hours.

It took until April 1974, before women were officially allowed in the race—the idea previously being that the marathon distance was just too strenuous for women. But now, women are running in such numbers that there is a growing group of "women-only" marathons. And heroes of their own, like tiny, 42-year old Japanese born Miki Gorman, who has won the women's division of the Boston twice.

Husbands and wives now run marathons, as well as jog together, and many times are joined by children. A California youngster, Mary Etta Boitano, turned in a 3-hour, 1-minute, 26-miler, and 14-year old Tommy Paris, son of Dr. Sam Paris of Syracuse, New York, who also runs marathons, ran "Boston" in 1976 in 3-hours and 10-minutes.

GROUPS

I personally think that much is to be gained by families who run together—a certain spirit of play that is shared, of exertion that is endured and understood, of accomplishment. Yes, the family that plays, (or runs) together stays together. For years, my wife Norma and I have jogged together.

In San Francisco, there's even an organization that encourages the family concept of running. Dozens of families, are enrolled in the Pamakids Club—which name stands for (you guessed it!) "pa, ma and kids."

In Palo Alto, California, a proposed ordinance that would have banned jogging on the city's streets, was defeated after motorists complained to the town council that hundreds of joggers sometimes five and six abreast, would block traffic and refused to leave the streets. In winning, the joggers had to agree to stop running "en masse" down the middle of the streets. And a committee has been formed to prepare guidelines for organized jogging.

It's just one more example of the tremendous popularity of running. Obviously, other communities will soon have the same "problem." If things keep going this way, they may even start to ban automobiles in certain areas when they intrude on the joggers' right-of-way. Who'd have imagined that 10 years ago?

THE NEW CONCEPT

I guess if you had to pinpoint a time when running first started to become popular, it was about a dozen years ago. Before that, it was largely for that special breed of men interested in racing and record-setting.

One of the most significant, (but often overlooked), influences was Percy Wells Cerutty, an Australian who ran a camp for distance runners.

Cerutty preached not only dedication and conditioning for running, but also total fitness of the spirit and mind, and the need for proper nutrition. One of Percy's most famous pupils was Herb Elliott, who won the 1,500 meters in the 1960 Olympic Games. But he had influence upon others—among them myself. I'll get into some of Cerutty's valuable ideas later in the book.

Most coaches trained their runners to run a fairly fast pace for their distance, coupled usually, with interval workouts; fast sprints interspersed with rest-walks. An Olympic team coach from New Zealand, Arthur Lydiard, sent his runners on long, slow jogs of 20 miles or so mixed (according to the season), with the speed work. It was Lydiard's concept that this LSD (long slow distance) built and maintained a level of stamina that, coupled with speed-fitness, paid off in victory. His most famous student was Peter Snell, an Olympic double winner at 800 and 1,500 meters in the 1964 Tokyo Games. Lydiard travelled across the United States and gave talks, telling of his new concept "jogging."

In 1962, Bill Bowerman, coach of the University of Oregon, travelled to New Zealand, met with Lydiard, "experienced" jogging, and returned to Oregon, full of praise for this new method. That area already was running-conscious, and from there, the word was spread to a nation beginning to search for fitness.

A man that I think helped to encourage the jogging movement was President Kennedy, who paved the way with his interest in youth and better health. At that time, I dedicated a 250-mile run from New York City to Washington, D.C. to his physical fitness program.

BODY TYPE

In all my years (and miles) of running I've often been asked, "Is there a preferred body type if you want to be a runner?" To which I answer a resounding "No!" The stereotype is that distance runners are tall and lean (like me) and the sprinters short and muscular. This may be generally true at the world-class level, but I've known a lot of stocky fellows who could run forever and lean men who were as quick as the best.

That's one of the beauties of the runner, or jogger; he comes in all sizes, shapes, ages, sexes, and professions. The best of athletes condition themselves with a program of running, and I know a lot of so-called "weekend athletes", (tennis players, golfers, you name it), who now do the same. They are assured of fitness with running and can better enjoy their sport. Or, if you prefer, their profession.

If you're worried what the neighbors will think when they see you out there running around the block or in the park, just remember that you're in good company, millions of people from all walks of life now jog or run.

CELEBRITIES

Some of the famous people I know (or know about) who run for joy and fitness are the astronaut John Glenn, a friend of mine; Senator William Proxmire (of Wisconsin), who runs to his office every morning in Washington, D.C.; California Senator Alan Cranston, who runs sprints in masters' meets; and show business people like Farrah Fawcett Majors, Robert Merrill, Charlton Heston, Jill Clayburgh, Robert Redford and Yul Brynner. The latter, incidentally, jogs backwards in order to exercise muscles that most people never reach.

One of the better "famous" runners is Eric Segal, author of the book "Love Story," who for years has competed in the Boston Marathon. And many people don't know that Bobby Riggs, the tennis player, beat me in a special challenge run across Death Valley a couple of years ago—although I gave him a 25-mile head start, in a 50-mile run.

SUPER FIT

A while back, I trained with John Landy, the second man (after Bannister) to run the mile in under four minutes. And I can distinctly remember suggesting to Derek Clayton—who still holds the world-record time for a marathon—2 hours, 8 minutes, 33 seconds set in 1969—that he ought to move up out of the middle distances to the longer races.

Historically, I suppose the most famous runner was Pheidippides, a foot soldier in the Greek army when they fought the invading Persians back about 500 B.C., near the plains of Marathon. When the Greek victory was secured, Pheidippides, who had a reputation for being a fast runner, was sent to carry the news to Athens. He ran (or jogged?) the 40 kilometers (about 25-miles), fell at the feet of his elders near the Acropolis, gasped "Rejoice! We conquer!" and died.

If reports of his death in this way are true, the Greeks certainly could have benefitted by today's training methods. I've known a lot of runners (myself included), who would hardly be taking a "deep breath" over that distance.

Not too many people perhaps remember, but from the turn of the century up through the 1920s, marathon runners were considered heroes in America. As the standard of living improved, and more leisure time became available, other sports gained attention. And the super heroes became professional competitors that people watched perform in stadiums, on courts and courses.

I think now that we've come full-circle, back to more of the virtues of the marathon man, including the realization that we too, can be that "marathon man" (or woman) if we are willing to expend the time and energy. Short of that, we can at least be super fit through a sensible program of jogging and running, as we will be suggesting in this book.

If people like Alfred Ventrillo, who completed the Boston Marathon though blind and 62, and Pete Strudwick, who ran up Pikes Peak despite the fact that he has no feet, can excel within their capabilities, so can you!

And the time to start is NOW . . . if you already haven't.

3

WHAT EQUIPMENT?

The Basics - Plus

If you're a fan of the Olympic Games, you probably know about the 1960 marathon run.

The finish that year was down the famed Appian Way and under the Arch of Constantine. Rome in all its historic glory.

A full moon illuminated the crowded streets during the closing stages of the late-evening race. Suddenly, into view, came the leader (and eventual winner), an unknown 28-year-old Ethiopian, a member of Emperor Haile Selassie's imperial guard, named Abebe Bikila.

The crowd buzzed with excitement, awed by how fit and fresh the runner seemed as he neared the end of his 26-mile,

385-yard ordeal in Olympic-record time—well over seven minutes faster than Emil Zatopek's 1952 mark.

But a good part of the crowd's excitement also had to do with the fact that Bikila was running over the Appian's cobblestones "barefoot" . . . that's right, without shoes. Here, was some kind of a Superman, for all the others wore shoes, didn't they!

Yes they did! At Bikila's level, and especially over cobblestones, it was unusual.

I myself won the Australian 10-mile championships during the 1950s, running barefoot on the grass. Both John Landy and Herb Elliott trained often without shoes. In fact, quite a few foreign joggers run barefoot on the beaches, woodlands, and even on golf courses.

Bikila himself explained later that it wasn't at all unusual for runners in his country to train without shoes, as you can cover more steps per minute (foot speed) barefoot.

The reality, however, is that people today are conditioned from birth on by the society they live in. Most of us have grown up wearing shoes, and to revert to barefoot is to change our biomechanical relationship with the ground. In other words, the feet work differently when they are covered so as to protect against hurtful surfaces (like concrete); and by suddenly going barefoot over a distance, we can disrupt a balance we're accustomed to and cause injury and pain to the feet and legs.

Shoes, then, are very important to the jogger—by far his most vital piece of equipment. If, as they say, an army travels on it's stomach, then a runner "survives" on his footwear.

One of the beauties of the sport is that you can get by with a fairly small amount of equipment. You can dress as inexpensively as you wish, using some of the things you already have. Or you can go out and buy all the latest clothes, and they come in a variety of prices depending on the quality, styles and where you shop.

If you're going to enter a race, there are certain standards of dress, yes, but it really doesn't matter how you look while you're beginning or training for that competition. A basic rule is; whatever is comfortable; to your taste; to your pocketbook; and to your body, is what you should choose.

Some beginners skimp on the price and care of their running shoes (not recommended)—or, instead, use the old tennis shoes (especially not recommended).

But remember, it's been calculated that each shoe lands on the ground about 800 times during a mile run. And so over a distance of miles, and depending on the person's weight, your shoes must be able to accomodate tons of weight. The more durable the shoe, the more comfortable and able to withstand shock, the better it is for your health and running ability.

Besides which, you aren't Abebe Bikila.

Having run across all sorts of surfaces and in all kinds of weather, I believe that I know about what equipment works best.

What follows is an appraisal of the equipment you'll need (and won't need), and how best to utilize it, for happy running days.

I might add that because of the tremendous interest in jogging and running, manufacturers are coming out with new wrinkles (no pun intended) all the while, so it's not a bad idea to periodically check with your local sporting goods, jogging-shoe, or department store.

Also, each October's issue of Runner's World magazine has an excellent guide as to what's the latest, and best, in jogging shoes.

SHOES

There is an old expression that says: "If the shoe fits . . . " It can mean a lot of things not footwear-related, but I know of nowhere that's more applicable than in the matter of running, or jogging shoes.

I want to tell you right here and now, that fit is just about "everything." If you run as much as you're supposed to, and considering the amount of pounding and rubbing your shoes will "absorb" in the process, the importance of fit can't be stressed often enough.

Stated simply, if your feet feel like a pair of hot coals and your knees, shins, calves, ankles, etc. are in a more-or-less constant state of discomfort or pain, bordering on injuries, you aren't going to run. At least not very far, and certainly not very often. Think about it!

For starters, let's take a hypothetical trip to the store—either the kind of specialized place in many cities that carries most every kind of jogging and running shoe, or a sporting goods store that has a few of the better-known, less-expensive type shoes. I'll leave it up to you to decide what fits your current stage of progress in running, as well as your product-buying-pattern.

Before you go, you'll want to bring along the socks you're going to wear (we'll discuss socks later) because they are an important part of fit. Make sure they're clean and won't wrinkle when you slip on the shoes. After you try on the shoes, "jog" in place around the store to get a feel of their fit, and how comfortable they really seem.

If you have any doubt whatsoever at this point, it's best to set them aside and make other choices. Be a skeptic and be sure. Also, if you just don't like their looks, it's probably best to reject them. Looks aren't going to make your feet feel any better or worse, but most people take a certain pride in style and appearance, and most likely you will too.

Now down to specifics. The fit of the shoe, in my opinion, should vary according to your intended purpose. If you choose to run longer distances—let's say over three miles—you want room between your big toe and the end of the shoe. That's because as you run farther the feet swell.

But if your preference is the shorter distances—a half-mile up to three—I believe you should go for a snug fit. And snug doesn't mean cramped. A snug fit helps reduce the shoe-against-skin friction which can cause blisters.

The contour of the bottom of the shoe should coincide with the shape of the bottom of your feet, of course. And you want a shoe that passes the "flex test"—looser at the front end, firmer at the rear.

Extremely critical is the arch support. You can usually

tell after two or three miles of running whether or not the metatarsal bond of the foot shows strain. If so, you're setting yourself up for injury to the legs unless you remove the arch support. A lot of people will try to replace the regular arch support with something they buy at a drugstore or shoemaker's. But I believe that you should go straight to a qualified podiatrist—meaning one who's himself a runner—and let him fit you. It'll cost quite a bit more, to be sure, but the savings in your health will be well worth it.

Most of us have always worn heels, and thereby our achilles tendons and calves are shortened by this. So you want a jogging shoe that has a good supportive heel, meaning wide enough; and one with the heel elevated—at least no lower than your regular shoes. Make sure the heel isn't too high, however, so it won't push you forward awkwardly.

The sole should provide traction, flexibility, cushioning, and protection. Nowadays, the shoe companies are bringing out all sorts of designs that are a departure from the old "flats." They go by names like waffle tread, star design, suction cup, brush sole, racing profile, grip plug, track spike studs, saw profile, octopus, star studded, and herring bond, to name a few.

Each has its selling points and you'll probably need to consult the clerk about advantages and disadvantages. I think durability is important, and if you're over 40 you'll want enough cushioning to protect against injury; younger runners can usually get by in lighter shoes. As can women.

If you're only doing a couple of miles a day, on a softer surface like grass, you may be able to utilize a less sturdy, inexpensive shoe. But as you advance into the category of six to ten miles a day on the road, you'll want something that has more substance.

A lot of runners prefer a heavier shoe for training and a lighter variety for racing. They'll own both "training flats" (as they are called) and "racing flats." The racing flats usually have soles that are thinner and, often, more stylized.

A sole that is TOO THICK can cause or aggravate injuries. But it's been my experience that many marathon runners opt for "too thin" in their choice of racing shoes. They may go faster during the early part of the 26-mile grind, but during the last five miles—when the going is toughest—a more supportive sole that better absorbs shock is worth it's weight in gold. It could be the difference between pulling up lame or finishing in a blaze of glory.

Nylon uppers have just about cornered the market, replacing the leather uppers of yesteryear. The nylon's cost less and are softer. In the past year or so, manufacturers have come out with the mesh upper that allows the foot to breathe more and is cooler. I think it's the better shoe, especially when longer distances are going to be run.

Another big development is the expanded variety of women's shoes. Women's feet tend to be narrower than men's, and for years many women were forced to accommodate to the wider men's shoes. That's no longer true.

As you continue to use your "new" shoes, they will, of course, show wear and tear. Some experienced runners believe that you should patch worn-down heels with one of the many applications available for sale. I personally disagree, because shoes when repaired tend to get out of their original balance and this again sets up possible injuries.

If you're going to run happily and successfully, you must realize that your shoes will be in need of more-or-less constant replacement. You should "never" let the heels (or soles) wear down too much before you buy other shoes.

It's a wise idea, used by many joggers, to be breaking in a newer pair of shoes while you're wearing out the older. In that way, you never miss a step on the route to continuing fitness and without foot failure.

CLOTHING

You can get about as fancy as suits your needs, in the matter of jogging clothes. Of course, you'll need a pair of shorts, and perhaps a light T-shirt and/or fishnet vest, plus a warm-up suit or (as they used to be called) sweatsuit. I prefer cotton, wherever possible, to nylon because it seems to allow for better body breathing.

When it's warm—even in a warm rain—I believe that the fewer clothes, the more the skin is able to feed itself on the oxygen in the air. The skin needs to breathe, just as the body's lungs. On a sunny warm day, I personally like to use only a pair of shorts when I jog. Of course, it's important immediately afterwards to slip on your warmup suit so that you won't catch cold. One thing you definitely don't want is tight, inhibiting clothing.

Contrarily, when it's very cold you want to bundle up like an Eskimo—well, almost. In fact, I suggest thermal underwear, a warmup suit, a ski cap—the works. When it's REALLY COLD you aren't out to set any records or heat the body to excess. You just want to keep moving.

Wear a long-sleeve fish-net vest when it's cold (if you don't choose thermals). And a trick I've learned that helps me to prevent stomach cramps, which has a tendancy to occur on a cold, windy day when you're running, is to put plain brown paper next to the stomach, between the skin and your underclothing. Also, several layers of lighter clothing can, in fact, be warmer than a couple of layers of the heavier, if you choose that route.

I've also found that, for men, jockey shorts don't rub the wrong way, as some jockstraps have a tendency to do. Women, of course, should wear a bra, but one that isn't so tight-fitting that it's uncomfortable.

Socks that fit well and aren't wrinkled inside the shoe and that absorb the sweat are very important in keeping the feet in good condition. They should be cotton, light, and white, because dye tends to get into the cracks of the feet. And socks must be laundered often. They are a big factor in the prevention of blisters.

Some runners like to wear sweatbands on their forehead to soak up perspiration that might run into their eyes. A better method I've found, is to tie a soaking-wet handkerchief around your hand and wipe off the perspiration. Another trick is to have some cologne or aftershave lotion on the handkerchief and every once in a while dab it under your nose. It helps clear the head, which can get pretty clouded during the heat of a long run.

OTHER ACCESSORIES

Some runners think that a stopwatch is an absolute necessity. If you have the money, fine, but unless you're going to be competing and will be doing time trials during workouts, an ordinary wristwatch with a second hand will be all you really need. A watch can be used to take your pulse rate, as well as give you a general idea of how fast you are jogging.

By the same token, I don't believe you need a foot counter (also known as a pedometer) which registers how many miles you've run. Enjoy your running. Things like stopwatches and foot counters have a tendancy to "scientifically" force you to a level beyond where you should be at, in accordance with your development. That time will come.

On another matter, I'm a firm believer in keeping a diary. Record the thoughts you have before, during, and after runs; also, all improvement ideas you learn from other sources. I also think that it is important to keep a "log" of the mountain of mileage you pile up in training, as well as in any competition.

With a permanent, complete record of all your running, you can look back a few years from now and you'll be absolutely amazed at how many miles those legs of yours have travelled. It's also great (mental) therapy to trace your progress. I know, I've been keeping logs for thirty years.

4
WHEN TO RUN

A Time That Fits
Your Needs

Whenever I give one of my "Running For Physical Fitness" talks, I can expect someone in the audience to ask this question:

"Bill, when's the best time to run?"

The question is certainly a good one, and more often than not is accompanied by a statement on, how busy a life this person leads. He, or she, finds it difficult to find that extra hour—or whatever—to fit running into the schedule. Better yet, they are looking for that "magic moment" when the planets are in conjunction, the weather is near-perfect, and the heavens have decreed all's right with the world. In short, they are almost expecting a miracle to get them through the self-motivation and determination required to start running.

My answer is that there is no magic moment. You should run as you feel, and when you feel that it best suits your life-style—however busy. To be a successful runner, you must make a genuine commitment that running will be a basic part of your life, so that the time set aside for running will be of great importance in relation to other activities in your life.

And, furthermore, you must run regularly, and if nature creates rain, sleet, snow, winds, sparkling sunshine, or the darkest of clouds, you still run. The only cautions I might make here are extreme heat or cold, and of the two, heat is most dangerous. When the thermometer rises to 85 degrees fahrenheit and above, it's time to store the running gear in the closet until the day (or heat wave) passes.

Of course, if you're accustomed to these temperatures, or are in super shape, go ahead. But be careful; heat stroke brought on by a never-say-quit jogger (the opposite of our "magic moment" man) can kill. In fact, at least one interested runner-historian, who covered the route and considered the time of year and day, has concluded that our Greek soldier friend Pheidippides died of heat stroke after running his Marathan and delivering his famous message—"Rejoice! We conquer!"

TIME OF DAY

I personally prefer the late-afternoon-to-early evening part of each day for my run. By then, most of my work has been done, and I'm ready to work off some of the day's tensions. I am with many others in choosing early evening as my running time. I understand that Dr. Ken Cooper of "Aerobics" fame runs every day at 5 o'clock in the afternoon.

But I have friends who choose the noon hour. They slip away to a nearby park, school track, perhaps an athletic club, and rather than eating (or drinking) a gigantic lunch, they jog. A light lunch may follow, or they may just skip it altogether.

The early morning, before work, is a third time period. For a lot of people it holds several advantages. One, especially if you live in the city, is that the air is at its cleanest then. Not many cars are already in the city, spewing out unhealthy exhaust fumes for the jogger to inhale.

In case you didn't already know it, the carbon monoxide from these fumes doesn't leave the body as readily, as carbon dioxide—it takes nearly eight hours for half the "monoxide" in your system to disappear. And that certainly isn't good. Extreme doses of carbon monoxide, of course, can be lethal.

People who run in the morning often tell me that for them, it's like putting money in the bank. They rise out of bed, slip on their gear, and almost before they've had time for second (and possible discouraging) thoughts, the day's run is completed. Other than having to get up early, the chief drawback I see in an early-morning schedule is that there seems to be less time to be leisurely.

And then there are those folks—I call them night owls—who run later at night, some by preferance, others by necessity. Even as late as midnight, or hours of 1 or 2 a.m. in the morning. If this is your running time, then wear a reflective vest, or at least light color clothing, that can be seen more readily by a passing motorist. Or, if you're running in a park, make sure it's not one that's known as a "junkies' hangout. You might even carry a whistle, or other protection objects, just in case. For women, it's probably best not to tempt fate—at least not alone. If you saw the television-movie that starred Joanne Woodward as the marathon-jogger-heroine, you'll know what I mean.

SACRED HOUR

Once you have found the time of day that fits you best, it's very important to try and make it a habit. That should be your "sacred hour", or 45 minutes, not to be disrupted by anyone or anything. Studies show that people who skip around from noon one day, to early evening the next, to morning the third, are the most likely to fail at running.

It's also important to not make your running a rush hour. You need time to put on your outfit, warm up properly, do your (jogging or running) unwind, bathe or shower, and change back into street clothes. You should also try to set aside a little time to just sit around thinking, or being otherwise creative, as well as for eating.

Speaking of eating, I think it's wise to wait at least an hour after your run before you take any food. And give yourself at least three to four hours after you eat before you try to run, because the blood is busy taking care of the food in the stomach. After it's finished there, you can use it, for your legs during the run. Something else: if you do run in the later evening, it's wise to allow the body at least an hour to unwind before you go to bed.

BENEFITS

Now: how often do you need to run in order to get the benefits that you are seeking? For excellent fitness and health I maintain that you should do an hour's running every day. If not an hour, then a half-hour, or 15 minutes. The minimum for any semblance of fitness should be five miles of running per week. If you jogged 10-minute miles, that means two 20-minute sessions plus one of 10 minutes a week or five 10-minute daily runs.

There are differing opinions as to whether running should be a daily ritual. A lot of doctors and other experts say, yes, keeping active on a running level should be accomplished every day; not necessarily the same amount of jogging each day, but jogging.

For example, if your time is limited by your work hours during the week, you might go for shorter runs then and save a long, more leisurely jog or run for the weekend. I personally think the plan of a longer run on the weekend is excellent.

Others contend that the body needs more rest in-between-runs. They suggest every other day—in other words, run one day, rest the next. Or perhaps three times a week. Still another approach is two days of running followed by one day of rest. In any event, I suggest that you follow the schedule that best fits your physical and psychological needs; a schedule that you can maintain on a regular basis.

HEAT AND COLD

It used to be that you could tell the arrival of spring and approach of summer by the robins that suddenly appeared everywhere. Now, the surest sign seems to be the number of joggers who come out of hibernation.

To repeat, my personal belief is that running should be a year-round activity. In certain parts of the country, such as California, where I live, the climate is more conducive to all-year-round jogging. I for one, certainly know how difficult it is to venture outside when it's 10 degrees below, and there's a sheet of ice or snow on your running path. It takes that special breed of man or woman to even consider it.

But running against the elements of nature can be a special challenge and thrill. I know. I've run in the blast-furnace heat of Death Valley and I've battled the icy blasts of Tazmania's "Mountain of Death," Mt. Wellington. Not long before I made the latter run, two men had died from exposure during a marathon, and in Death Valley, California, a women whose car had stalled, died when she tried to walk for help.

If you do run in extremely cold weather, I suggest that as you approach the end of your journey, you take extra caution to gradually slow down, thus curtailing chances for a chill. And, when finished, change immediately out of your clothes. Sitting around in them is an open invitation for a bad cold, or worse.

Extreme heat is the opposite end of concern. Even if you're jogging in your birthday suit (you know, the one you were born with) you're going to sweat a lot causing the body to overheat and setting up a likelihood of cramps, heat exhaustion, and even maybe heat stroke. Dr. Ken Cooper, in fact, has stated that 98 degrees fahrenheit is an absolute maximum that anybody should risk a vigorous (and lengthy) run.

I went contrary to this by jogging in temperatures that got as high as 120 degrees in Death Valley, but I'm not suggesting that for anybody else. And you have to remember, I was super fit (still am!), well-prepared, had plenty of support people along in case of trouble, and I took it slow and frequently stopped for rest and liquids.

If the temperature is in the 90s and you insist on going out for a training (or even competition) run, drink a glass of water or two before you set out and another glass every 15 or 20 minutes. Its' very important to keep replacing the fluids that your body loses. You can cool down, too, by pouring water over your head and the rest of your body. You see marathoners doing it all the time during a race.

SNOW AND RAIN

Running when it's snowing or raining can be a delight. The air is cool, fresh, exhilarating under these conditions, and the body seems to respond with more than it's usual energy. It also gives you an opportunity to shout to the world (and to the less-brave-runners): "I'm tough, nothing can stop me."

Keep a closer eye on the ground if you run during rain or snow and change out of your wet clothes immediately afterwards. For me, the misty moments of a light rain or a new snowfall, especially, in a jogger's life aren't to be missed. There's a certain fantasy-like feeling when skimming across new-fallen snow.

If it's a real pouring rain or the snowfall is a blizzard, you most likely would want to stay inside, and I can't say I blame you. As in all else in life, common sense should dictate whether you run or not under certain weather conditions. Obviously, it doesn't make good sense to run when there are high gusty winds, thick fog, or during a thunderstorm.

WIND

Sudden gusts can be dangerous. In 1968, when I was running the 125 miles across Death Valley, I encountered a sandstorm. As is my way, I forged on, even though I was practically blinded by the sand swirling in the air around me. Then, quicker than the flash of mother nature's anger, I was lifted up by a gust of wind and dropped some 15 feet down the road. Luckily, I wasn't hurt, and I picked myself up and continued. But believe me it was an experience I won't soon forget. It scared the wits out of my wife Norma, who was accompanying me nearby in a car.

Always remember that it takes something like six per cent more oxygen to run into a headwind of almost a dozen miles per hour, and you'll be jogging at a slower pace. Don't expect to run at the same speed that you are accustomed to under normal circumstances. But you'll get as good a workout, provided you don't "slow down" in your efforts to jog at your usual pace.

One trick is to run against the wind early (if you can arrange it) when you're not as tired and then let the wind sweep you home, as if you were running the last lap in the Olympic Games. With the wind pushing, you'll find that your stride naturally lengthens . . . so let it. Any "time" that you've lost running into a headwind on the way out, can be more than made up coming back via tailwind.

As a matter of fact, of all the conditions I love to run under, it's with the wind that rates near the top of the list. I suppose I enjoy it so much because it gives the feeling of such freedom of foot. It's like running downhill, which we'll get into during our next chapter on "Where To Run."

5

WHERE TO RUN

Looking At All
The Possibilities

For years, a favorite enjoyment of mine has been to share "where-type" running stories with other runners.

Of course, if you've been running as long as I have, you're bound to have plenty of unusual experiences.

For example, years ago while running in Australia, I unintentionally intruded too near and was, in turn, chased by a kangeroo.

Are they dangerous, you ask? You bet! One swipe of their paw could smash your face in. I quickly climbed the nearest tree.

In Canada, on a lonely road near Lake Louise, a big bear suddenly loomed a few feet ahead of me. I didn't even say hello. I must have broken the four-minute mile, as I wheeled and ran from there like greased lightning. It has occurred to me that, running in fright, can make most anyone an Olympic champion.

I suppose I've jogged in one fashion or another, in as many countries on as many different terrains, as anybody ever has: across the Alps of Switzerland, on the moors of Scotland, along the canals of Holland, down the boot of Italy, through the cluttered cities of Asia.

I was once arrested in Vienna for running on the sidewalk in my shorts (can you imagine that) and run off the road in England by a mad motorist determined to add a jogger's shorts to his collection. One late night in Australia I spotted a UFO—a sight verified the next day by several others who'd seen the same thing.

But you know what: of all countries, the United States affords the greatest variety in weather conditions and terrain, the lowlands of Florida, the snow and ice of Minnesota, the deserts of California (Death Valley), the tall timber of the Pacific Northwest and the fog of San Francisco.

Part of the great joy of running, then, is that there is beauty to be found in almost every locale—if you are "tuned in" to it.

It used to be that quite a few potential joggers, (especially women), were very hesitant about stepping outdoors and jogging once around the block. What will the neighbors think? Maybe I'll be attacked? Or hit by a car?

Happily, that attitude is largely a thing of the past. However, if you still are a bit shy, you can jog in place in your apartment, or even the back yard.

JOGGING INDOORS

Friends of mine who travel, often run in place in their hotel room when they don't have time to get outside, or when they are concerned about jogging in a strange city. Many times, I have jogged motel stairs and lobbies.

What you do is count the number of steps you take in

travelling a mile and then run in place until your feet (800 each foot) hit the floor that many times.

Or you can prefigure the amount of time it takes you normally to jog a mile and then, watch in hand (or clock on the wall), run in place for that long.

All this, of course, is scientific but it's also tedious. It lacks joy, and only the most dedicated of joggers are usually willing to persevere under this kind of a regimen. Also, unless you're on grass (and I don't mean smoke) it can be hard on the legs.

If you still insist on staying inside, a gymnasium or athletic club might be just what the doctor ordered. They are, for the most part, free of pollution, and a great retreat when it's below zero outside and the wind is whistling in the rafters.

Some, in fact, border on the fabulous. The Los Angeles Athletic Club, for one, has a 165-yard track that is 11-2/3 laps to the mile banked, and an excellent spot to get a good workout. I've been there often. Ditto the New York Athletic Club and their wooden track.

Yet, many tracks aren't what I'd call prime running places. For one thing, when you have to go in circles too many times (say, 20-plus) it can make you dizzy watching the same scenery. And that's a lot of corners for your knees to be negotiating—on a hard surface, yet.

If you "must" work out at the club (after all, you HAVE paid) I'd say it's wise to alternate running directions from day to day, so as to avoid the orthopedic difficulties that can arise from going too often across a surface sloped one way. Many clubs already have "clockwise" and counter-clockwise days for running.

To counteract the dizzying boredom of going around in circles, try running with a friend. Unless you're doing wind sprints, or there's a rule against two abreast, you can get in some good conversation while jogging on an inside track.

Also, you can create greater interest by making up games: such as "racing" on or around the heels of others on the track; cutting up and down the "banked boards"; imagining you're pounding down the stretch of the Olympic stadium finals. It all works, believe me. Running is part mental, including a good deal of imagination.

RUNNING OUTDOORS

This same sense of imagination comes in handy if you're considering working out at an outdoor track—say at the local high school or the college in your vicinity. Some colleges have modern-day artificial surfaces, such as UCLA in West Los Angeles, where I often run.

But for the most part these 440-yard (or 400-meter?) ovals will be dirt, cinder, crushed brick, whatever, and four laps to the mile. Again, you'll have to fight the feeling of being on a treadmill. It can create what I call a "mental tiredness", even though you're feeling great physically.

Another problem is that these ovals, measured to the inch, are distance-oriented. In Chapter 7, I'll take up the point that if you're just rounding into condition, you don't want to think distance; you want to think "time spent" doing different disciplines.

However, these facilities are outdoors (a plus), and you don't have to follow the "circle." You can jog on the grass infield, or maybe just take off onto the school grounds, or thereabouts. UCLA's track stadium has a hill nearby that's famous for making champions out of the otherwise just-excellent.

If you are at the point where you wish to clock your fitness for distance, a track, of course, is your destination. It's also a good spot for interval-type training, that I will discuss in a later chapter.

CITY STREETS

Where you live is a big determining factor in where you'll most-often run. If there are no parks nearby and the nearest school is several miles down the road, it is most likely that you'll take to the streets, or what I sometimes call the "concrete-jungle".

Street running, of course, is fraught with all kinds of obstacles, and I don't recommend it if you can possibly get to a park, school, the beach, or a nature trail. It does, however, beat inactivity and running in place in your living room.

In street running, the pavement is hard on your legs; so be sure you wear well-cushioned shoes. You'll also have to sometimes contend with many people along your path, as well as dogs who seem to take delight in running after or with you, or just barking at you.

But far worse than the possible problems of dogs, is the war being waged between motorists—fighting to dominate the streets—and joggers who want their fair share of space.

I can understand that when joggers run four and five abreast, it can be a bit much in certain areas and should be controlled. But I just can't understand motorists who use their car as if to threaten a runner, or who heap abuse on the runner, as they speed by.

PARKS

Eventually, of course, laws that accommodate joggers' needs will have to be enacted. Part of the solution might be more jogging paths in the parks, and alongside our road-ways.

The state and city governments, I feel, owe it to the health of the people to get involved. Right now, it's estimated that about 23 million people are into jogging and running in one form or another, with many more millions joining every year.

A lot of parks are already creating trails for joggers, or measuring off sections that just naturally lend themselves to running. Some have courses with obstacle "stations." You jog from station to station, stopping at one for situps, then on the next for chinups, and so on. I suppose this is a noble attempt, but people I've talked with say many runners just jog right by the stations, not wishing to be "interrupted."

I'm a firm believer in the variation of scenery, and you get a lot of that in parks. Some smaller community parks, of course, are barely big enough to circle before you have to go around them again. But the larger parks in some cities are a joggers' joy forever.

Central Park in New York City is one of my favorites. You can run on the soft, tan track, that previously only horses used, circle the half-mile around the reservoir, or run on the beautiful paths.

In fact, the world seems to be filled with parks made for running: Stanley Park in Vancouver; Griffith Park in Los Angeles; Hyde Park in London; Golden Gate in San Francisco, and many more throughout the world.

A special enchantment to me is Kapiolani Park in Honolulu, which has just about the right combination of undulating grass, a gentle island breeze, and softly swaying (in the distance) Hawaiian music. No wonder there's such a turn out there.

OTHER AREAS

I've always enjoyed running on golf courses, which again offer a feeling of next-to-nature plus variety of scenery. The problem is that with the proliferation of joggers, many courses are banning us. You can, still, run the outskirts of many; and if you get there early enough in the morning or after dark, you could even run from hole to hole, which is a kick. Fore!

The Europeans, especially in Finland and Sweden, run through the pine needle forests. The needles fall off the trees and form a sort of soft carpet which is great for barefoot, fartlek-type (we'll explain later) training. The great Finnish champions all used this method of preparation.

However, be careful about forests (the ones without pine needle paths). They're no problem if you watch your step, or don't run too long—or too often. But the terrain can be rough, and if you land in the wrong pot-hole or hit a twig, you could twist your ankle or fall. Also, the lack of a flattened surface tires the muscles more quickly and sets up the possibility of injury.

Personally, I like to fling off my shoes, put on a pair of swimming trunks, and gallop like a racehorse along the oceanfront. There are few feelings that rival it in euphoria ... the sand of Mother Nature at your feet, the spray of the ocear blowing in your face, the free flow of your body through space. And the wet sand definitely seems to stimu-ate the central nervous system as you glide across it.

You can sometimes get a good, strenuous workout in the deeper sand, away from the water's edge. But for the most part I avoid it. In the first place, it's no fun. In the second, you can often pull a leg muscle. If you wear shoes, sand gets in them; if you don't, the sand is often as hot as coals.

Running up and down hills strengthens the quadricep muscles of the legs and helps to increase cardiovascular capacity. But it can be very hard on the muscles, if you are not careful.

I'm not a great fan of city-downtown-type running. But if you're travelling, it's sometimes fun to map out (either yourself or by asking around) older, quaint sections of a city and then jog through their history and culture. Try to avoid spots where there are a great many traffic lights and the congestion of people, cars, or bicycles is very great.

Since variety is said to be the spice of life, why not make variety the spice of your running? A street run one day. In the park the next. The golf course, the country, wherever. Run near your home (or, even, to and from work) during the weekdays and head for greener areas for a jog on weekends.

But wherever you are, at home or away, in mountains or desert, on grass or on cobblestone, I hope I've made the point that—as a runner— you have the world at your feet.

Just think of the experiences you'll be enjoying that you can relate to friends, family and your fellow joggers and runners.

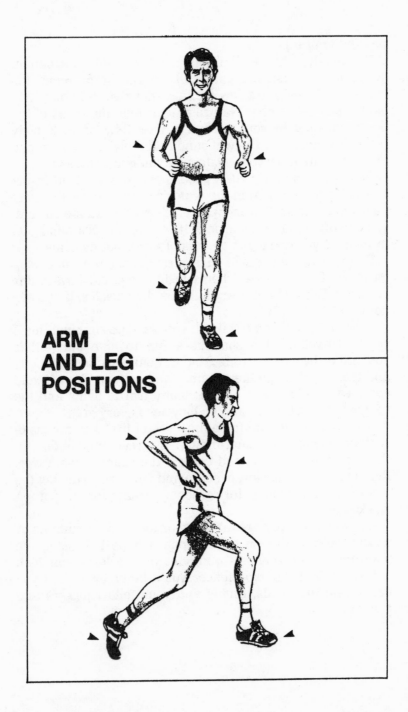

ARM
AND LEG
POSITIONS

6
HOW TO RUN
The Best Method

As the world explodes into becoming one gigantic jogging path, I suppose you could say I couldn't be happier. After all, I've been called the Messiah of ultra-long-distance running. I've been preaching the gospel now for more than 30 years. Not to mention running some 130,000 miles myself.

But I'm concerned that a lot of so-called joggers, or runners, don't know HOW to run. They know who's doing it (everybody), that it's good for them (the why), what equipment they'll need, and when and where jogging and running, best suits their style of living.

Yet, with many, there seems to be no guiding light, no plan of approach and action. It seems that there are a great many people who just go out and start running without any preparation whatsoever.

As a result, you'll sometimes hear about jogger-related difficulties. Or that the runner doesn't progress as quickly as he (or she) expected, gets into a rut and may even wind up quitting.

Most mistakes and difficulties can be avoided. There is a way to successfully start from scratch—or even if you've already been running—graduate into becoming a more knowledgeable and first-rate runner, totally in command of your progress.

You wouldn't, for example, launch into a new job without some idea of how to go about it. For some of the professions it takes years of schooling. Let's say you're going on vacation. Do you just jump in the car and take off—for anywhere? Most people I know have a goal, a destination. Somebody, some place they want to see is at the other end. They may already know the quickest, the best, direction. If not, they consult maps. They figure how long, what supplies they'll need, how much it'll cost. Only then do they start their journey.

Yet, this same otherwise intelligent person may just go out and, at random, start jogging. Others are doing it, right? Seems simple enough. Everybody knows HOW to run. You place one foot in front of the other at a pace faster than a brisk walk . . . Presto. You'll feel better, look younger, live longer. You'll be "getting fit."

Yes, running can be a simple matter, and you just may be the one who instinctively has good body mechanics and knows how to proceed from Point A to Point B in the most logical manner. But the chances are, you could benefit by techniques that have enabled me to master years of competitive (as an amateur) then professional running, without serious setbacks.

Part of the ability to succeed at almost anything is confidence, based on a knowledge of how, and given that sense of direction, or purpose. And so, I intend to tell you how you can map out a step-by-step program (Chapter 7) that within a year's time—if you follow it—will put you at a level of fitness others will envy (unless they, too, are following it).

Furthermore, if you run from the knees down, as I'll be suggesting in this chapter, you just might be able to pull off the entire project without too many sore muscles. Of course, I cannot guarantee it. Every body is different, and they all have their particular structural weaknesses.

MEDICAL CHECKUP

First, of course, you'll want a checkup from your physician, especially if you tend to be overweight and are over 40 years old and haven't been doing much exercise of a vigorous nature. But even if you are younger, and in shape, you might get a checkup—just in case.

Have your doctor look at your legs, your knees, the back, the feet and ankles. And, of course, your heart. I'd suggest a step, treadmill, or recumbrance test to insure there's nothing organically the matter with your pump (heart). Taking a complete "stress" test is certainly recommended for people with some ailment and if you are past 40. Tell your doctor your intention: super fitness by running. If you get a clean bill of health, you're ready to tackle the "how" of proper running.

SHUFFLING ALONG

I have the feeling that most people when young, were taught that "high knee action" is the proper way to run. And that you should spring off the balls of your feet as you run.

That may be all right if you are Houston McTear, trying to break nine seconds in the 100-yard dash. Collegiate, high school, or younger runners at play and who are racing distances under, say, a mile, all profit from this method. Even older runners in masters meets, if they are going the shorter distances, run with high knees and off the toes, or balls of the feet.

But for the jogger or marathon type whose goal is longer and slower distance—and above all to keep moving, high knee action is an open invitation to problem knees. And, of course, if you're going to keep those knees of yours low, you'll find you almost automatically are running flat-footed, which is what you want.

So, the approved Emmerton Method of getting fit and avoiding pain is to just shuffle along, (as I term it) landing flat-footed and raising the knee only high enough to sort of skim across the ground.

The basics of this method is that you take short strides. I, for one, have always believed that most runners take too long a stride, and when you're doing that on hard sidewalk and road surfaces, you're asking for injury. It may not be hurting now, but the knees (or back) will take such a pounding over a distance, that they will start to complain before too long.

What's that you say? You'd like a little more speed? You feel like a flat-footed Grandma Moses with your short stride and lowered knees? All well and good. You can speed up by quickening the stride; but keep it short. And keep those knees churning low. It may seem uncomfortable to you now, but believe me, if you're going to last until 100 (the age I expect to live to) this is the way.

I'm a firm believer in relaxed running. In fact, the key words in my style are "relaxed" and "economical." Relaxation of the mind and body; economy of the leg and foot movement.

As you're travelling along, you'll want to breathe deeply with the full diaphram. I mean, literally "shout it out!" The best example I can think of is the "whoosh!", or loud "grunt-shout" that shotputters let out, as they send the iron ball on its way out of their hand. Practitioners of the martial arts are big, too, with their sound "bursts," letting it all (the breath) out, as are many a tennis pro when serving.

This is not to say you have to sound like a steam engine. If you're self-conscious, you can try to keep the sound down while you are working the full diaphram. Whenever any runner challenges me about the subject, I remind him that you could hear Olympic champion Herb Elliott all over the stadium as he ran and "wooshed" his way to glory.

ARM AND LEG RHYTHM

The arms are an important factor in running. I like to vary arm positions as I go along. I'll let them hang at my sides, low down, for a while. Then, I might hold them high, above my waist. Being a "mechanical man" whose arms constantly stay in the same spot is tiring, not to mention boring. Rolling the shoulders also helps relax the body.

When you're running on flat territory the arms, of course, act as a balance mechanism. As the left leg strides forward, the right arm is out in front of the body, "balancing" the left leg. Then, when the right leg moves out front, the left arm balances it.

The arms and legs, too, must have a rhythm. One sure way of speeding up the stride (or throwing it out of kilter) is to speed up the action of the arms. And make sure you don't swing the arms side to side, across the body. You want them going back and forth past the hips at about a 90-degree angle just slightly in front (and in back) of the body.

When you've gone up (and down) as many hills and mountains as I have, you learn the best way of handling them, too. As you head uphill, you want to lean forward, taking the weight off the thigh and upper leg muscles.

Here, low leg action is especially helpful, and you want the arms low at all times. However, the arms don't balance as they do when you're on flat ground. Now, as the left leg strides forward, so too, does the left arm; when the right leg moves out front, the right arm accompanies it.

Going uphill is perhaps the least pleasurable (however beneficial fitnesswise) area of running because it's WORK, spelled with a capital W. But you can do it without great difficulty if you'll follow my method.

Contrarily, when you're moving back downhill, you want to lean your body backwards. This slows the pace and keeps you under control so that you don't suddenly act like a racing auto. And by using the same arm motion (and low leg action) as you did when going uphill, you'll also slow any tendancy to speed out of control.

I stress uphill and downhill action because careful, correct usage of proper technique can help prevent injuries that often afflict the unwary.

Also, I feel that the "shuffling along" approach is especially superior under bad-weather conditions. Being always closer in touch with the ground, you're less likely to slip and possibly hurt yourself.

YOUR EYES

One other thing: where do you "look" as you move ahead down the trails of jogging? Of course, you want to be aware of your general surroundings for potential hazards, but at the same time, you should be "drinking" in the beauty and good feelings the environment offers.

As far as specific eye contact, I usually focus on a spot on the ground 10 feet in front of me. But it's wise to occasionally "rest" the eyes by looking up and away. Who knows? You may feast those jogger's eyes upon some super attractive person who is admiring your style and perseverance.

SPEEDING IT UP

It goes without saying that my shuffle method has its limitations in the matter of speed. It's good for as fast as an 8-to-12 minute pace (or slower) and is the sort of a precaution I take when I'm doing one of my 50-mile-a-day stints across country.

I think it's excellent for the beginning jogger, the older jogger, and the jogger who's prone to injury. It's practically guaranteed to keep you moving, and if you do it long enough, hard enough, and often enough, it will keep you in excellent condition.

However, you may also want to incorporate other tempos into your running repertoire. By going faster, beyond "shuffle maximum," your knees will just naturally lift higher and you'll lengthen your stride.

You are still flat-footed, and running for the most part

from the knees down, but you've moved now into what I've called "fresh swing tempo." You can pick this swing tempo up to about as fast as you'd like, but remember: the faster you move, usually the higher the knee action required and the longer the stride . . . up to, of course, what your body structure and fitness will tolerate.

If you really start "driving" off your legs, with high knee action, long strides and being up on the balls of the feet, you're into sprinting. A sprint can be part of a serious runner's tempo, perhaps in segments of a race or as part of an interval fartlek-type workout (I'll explain these later).

But sprinting should be used judiciously, in my opinion. First, the legs must be really fit and strong to withstand the extra stress. Second, you shouldn't sprint over any extended distance—say not beyond 200 yards. Third, if you're up in years be particularly careful. And fourth, try not to sprint on hard (like cement) and/or uneven surfaces; nor surfaces that are slippery. Last but not least, don't do it when you are tired.

Grass can be a good surface to run hard (swing tempo, sprint) on; or maybe one of the softer dirt-types, such as tanbark or cinder. Many of the artificial tracks—outdoors and indoors—can be especially hard on the legs. Avoid any extended sprinting on them.

SLOWING IT BACK DOWN

If you've gone through a workout, changing tempo, a good way to slow it back down gradually before stopping completely, is the shake-up or shade-down if you prefer.

In it, you play like a loosely-jointed puppet on a string, as all the muscles are moved up and down. You can run in short, clipped steps, or with a regular rhythm. You jog on the toes and on the heels. Shake-ups can also be used as a warm-up device.

Another way to slow down is, simply, to walk. You walk in about the same manner as I've suggested doing the shuffle—except you're moving slower.

In our next chapter we'll get into a basic program (and other programs) that should help you attain fitness without suffering the aches and pains that many joggers have. It will be mostly aerobic training, though some anaerobics will also be used.

To define, aerobic means the slower type of running where the body's demand for oxygen doesn't exceed the supply. Marathons, jogging are in this category.

In anaerobic, the demand DOES exceed the supply. This is the so-called sprints, or bursts, where you run fast and are quickly out of breath.

Most running is a combination of the two. Mike Spino, with whom I spend time at an Esalen clinic in California several years ago, defines it this way in his book "Running Home":

—Marathon (26-plus miles): 95 per cent aerobic, 5 per cent anaerobic.

—100-Yard Dash: 5 per cent aerobic, 95 per cent anaerobic.

—Mile Run: 50 per cent aerobic, 50 per cent anaerobic.

For our purposes, there's an emphasis on aerobics. It's my basic approach, as you'll see by the upcoming programs. And it refers back to the idea that the longer you can run, the longer you can probably live.

7

A PROGRAM FOR YOU

From Basic To Advanced

Well, your starting day has arrived.

Time to put on the new outfit (or whatever you're going to wear), lace up those new shoes you bought, and begin the new running life.

It's time to quit theorizing and thinking about jogging and to put what you're learning—or already know—into results. The day has come to begin on that long trail toward running fitness.

All you need now is a program. We said in Chapter 6 that those with the best-laid plans always stand the best chance of succeeding. So, we're going to plot for "you," a course of action that will put a new bounce in your step.

Remember, though, there are no miracles. You're going to have to stay with us, step by step, as we proceed . . . slowly but surely. The game we're playing is patience.

I've been writing programs for people for many years and properly applied, I've seen them work wonders. Many of my programs have been individual approaches to a person's specific problems and interest.

I've also had great success with my basic program aimed at almost anybody who's interested in getting into shape. It's a three-to-six-month (choose one) program to be used as a starting—or restarting—point, and from which you can progress into areas that especially interest you.

Of course, the direction you'll eventually take depends on your age, where you live, the amount of time you're willing to devote, and whether you're more of a jogger-type or a competition-type.

But whether you will be jogging around the clock every day, or someday running a marathon, you need a strong foundation to build on. Our workouts are designed for the body to gradually adjust to increased stress.

As you're building, of course, you need a support system. By that I mean you'll have to get sufficient rest and sleep. Proper nutrition will be important . . . neither too much food, nor too little. And its also important to be in a positive frame of mind. If the pressure of your work is too heavy, or you're right in the middle of a personal crisis, it could be best to delay (but not too long) until things come together.

Applying the right amount of progressive stress can be very tricky. My program is aimed at building up the body faster than you are possibly breaking it down. Not enough sleep, poor nutrition, and over-workouts (that cause injuries) are all "negative stress" factors.

It can be taken as a general rule that as long as you feel well, sleep well, and enjoy your jogging, you are not over-stressing yourself. But if your sleep is poor, your coordination bad, or if you are perpetually tired and irritable, then you are certainly not at the right conditioning level.

I have known many joggers and runners, who during this phase became uptight and pushed themselves even harder to achieve, or "keep-on-schedule." This is a terrible mistake, sure to result in injuries or worse.

What you want, then, as we get into our basic program, is as painless, stress-less-start into the world of jogging and running, and that takes patience. Time is your ally and that being the case, you shouldn't be concerned about how many miles you do (or don't) go for now.

You are, however, interested in how long a time period you'll be devoting to each of our disciplines, so you'll want a watch. In Chapter 3, I suggested that a wristwatch with a second hand is sufficient. Or you can use a stopwatch if you prefer.

THE BASIC FITNESS PROGRAM
PHASE ONE

You start by walking five minutes. Let's say a somewhat brisk walk; or more slowly if you prefer.

At the end of this first five minutes you bend and stretch —loosening the joints, toning the muscles—for five minutes. Four such exercises that I've found beneficial are jumping jacks, touching the toes with the legs apart, a high knee lift, and shoulder roll. But there are others. We'll discuss them later. You might do a minute of each exercise with a slight rest in between, or one right after another.

Now comes your first running time. You jog slowly—real slowly—for five minutes. And that's all. Just five minutes. And then you top off the workout with another five-minute walk—about the same pace as the first.

Total time spent: 20 minutes

Phase One should last three weeks. I suggest a minimum of four days a week. Let's say, Monday, Wednesday, Friday, and either Saturday or Sunday.

Five (or even six) days could be more beneficial, of course. But I'm also a believer that the body needs rest to repair itself. At least one or two days a week, if not three. I'll leave it up to you to decide how you feel.

During these first three weeks you'll be improving the

muscle tone, strengthening the leg and back muscles, beginning to improve the state of your blood, and eliminating the toxins from your bloodstream.

Hopefully, you'll be avoiding the normal early-jogger stresses and pains. Even if you are already a jogger-runner of some mileage, you could try this program, and see how it benefits you.

Maybe you're just, now, running around the block without a sense of real direction. This could be it. Or you used to jog, got bored, busy, whatever, and might like to try a comeback.

I can't begin to tell you how many people I've known who raced right out and tried to run a mile or two—and became sore and stiff, or worse. Or who jogged along aimlessly for months without purpose. In either case it's bad news.

PHASE TWO

After the first three weeks have been completed, you're ready to move on to the second phase. It, again, lasts three weeks. But instead of 20 minutes the workouts are now for 30 minutes.

What you may be wondering is, if you've gone through three weeks of Phase One but didn't get in ALL the workouts (which would be a total of 12 at the minimum) should you go on to Phase Two.

My suggestion is to delay getting into Phase Two until you have gone through the complete basics. Remember, you're trying to build a strong foundation for your body and you shouldn't look for any shortcuts.

But try to keep on schedule. Rest, as I've emphasized, is very important, but if you're only able to get into workouts one or two days a week, you won't progress as rapidly as I've outlined.

Phase Two is broken down as follows:
—Walk five minutes.
—Bend and stretch for five minutes.
—Jog 10 minutes very easily; remember, the first phase was a five-minute jog.

—Walk three minutes.

—Jog seven minutes very easily.

Remember, there are still no thoughts of distance covered. And, now, as the leg muscles get stronger, your cardiovascular system should be improving. The weight should start dropping off, the muscle tone continue to improve, and the breathing easier. Your heart-beat recovery rate should also be better.

PHASE THREE

By now, all systems willing, you've been working out six weeks. Phase Three itself will be a six-week program. Each day's workout is for 40 minutes and goes as follows:

—Five minutes of walking.

—Five minutes of bending and stretching.

—30 minutes of nonstop jogging, or running, at a slow pace that is comfortable. Remember, still no distance is considered.

By now your pulse rate should be lowered. The cholesterol level should be down. Your endurance and stamina improved noticeably. Your energy level higher. The recovery rate good. And the muscle tone glowing, so as to give you what I call that "rainbow effect."

But you may also be getting weary of the constancy of routine, (kind of like the seven-year itch). But it's important to keep at it. Don't quit now, or start cheating. Keep setting aside this (exercise) time for your own well-being. Believe me, you won't regret it.

PHASE FOUR

You now have been at it for three months, up through the third phase. And, if a fair level of fitness is all you want, I suppose you could "stabilize" at the Phase Three program and use it for quite some time.

For example, you could interchange Phase Three with a

run to time, according to how you feel. Maybe: tonight I feel like 10 or 15 minutes around the block (or wherever). And the next night it might be 45 minutes—according to how you feel.

If you can, however, I'd now suggest running at least 25 to 60 minutes, five days a week (minimum four), with at least twice a week making an effort to run rapidly enough to push your pulse rate up to 145 beats a minute.

This just-mentioned "interchange plan" can also be interchanged with or after the completion of Phase Four, that goes as follows:

—Five minutes of walking
—45 minutes of nonstop jogging at a reasonably slow pace. You can increase the pace the last five minutes of this run. But the most important thing is that you keep on running.
—10 minutes of alternate walking and running. You walk one minute and follow it with a fast-paced one-minute run. Then you walk one minute again, and run another fast-paced minute. And so on for the next 10 minutes.
—Five minutes of walking to "cool down" and let the heart return to normal.

Phase Four is what I term the "hour-long," or 60-minute-workout. With the "cool-down" walk (and-or shakeups described in Chapter 6) it's actually 65 minutes.

This last phase is designed to be the "ultimate," or maximum in the basic program. You should work at it for three months. Then you're ready to jog wherever, and just about as long as you choose. Or you may want to enter some form of competition available to runners of all ages. Phase Four has qualified you (for the most part) for them.

PULSE RATE

An added note-during those fast-paced one-minute sprints of Phase Four, you should aim to get the pulse rate up to about 1ₓ0 beats a minute. You determine the beats-per-minute by feeling your pulse at the wrist—or, if you prefer, the carotid artery in the front of the neck that supplies blood to the head.

Count the number of beats for 15 seconds on your watch, and then multiply by four, or count the beat for 10 seconds and multiply by six. Or you can just count for the entire minute. You should also take your pulse rate during the one-minute walk periods.

The one-minute sprint-walk routine, of course, is one version of an anaerobic-aerobic regimen (remember, we defined these terms in Chapter 6). There are, of course, more advanced interval-training disciplines which we'll talk about later on.

The purpose of anerobic-aerobic alternating is to build up stamina and increase speed while improving the body to withstand greater strain. The body's fitness is revealed by the recovery rate, which of course will improve as you get into shape.

At the conclusion of a run—no matter how fast, or hard—the pulse rate should be back to normal after a 15-minute rest period.

AIMING HIGHER

When I was competing, I made it a point to push my body almost to the point of exhaustion, at least twice a week. And I still follow much the same principle of a very difficult workout at least twice a week. My body has come almost to "enjoy," or require it.

I've long had the feeling that most people—competitors and non-competitors alike—relax too soon in their pursuit of fitness. They find a level that's comfortable for them and stay there. What you should do, of course, is to aim higher. And higher. And higher still.

You can improve upon Phase Four by, of course, going faster during the jogging portion of the workout. Push it, just a little harder. And the more fit and confident you become, the faster you WILL want to run.

Another way of "aiming higher" is to speed up the one-minute anaerobic runs. Or increase them to two-minute runs followed by two-minute walks; or two-minute runs followed by one-minute walks. Maybe, instead of a 10-minute segment of one-minute alternates, you could do it for 20 minutes (10 runs, 10 walks). Let your ingenuity roam.

Instead of 45 minutes of nonstop jogging, do it for an hour, or 90 minutes, or whatever. And faster. But whenever you increase your non-stop period of running, it's always wiser to go slower at first, THEN speed it up to fit your comfort.

Handicapping yourself is a way of increasing strength. My friend Emil Zatopek, the Olympic champion, used to run in heavy boots so that when he got back into normal running shoes, they seemed light as a feather.

Zatopek was, I suppose you could say, somewhat of a fanatic in the matter of running. One story I like to tell is about the time when he was unable to get outdoors for his daily run. So he put his wife on his shoulders, stepped into the bathtub, and ran in place.

During all phases of your basic fitness program, I think it's a good idea to change scenery whenever possible. If you can avoid it, don't always work out in the same location, or even on the same surface. Change will help sustain your interest, and that's a good part of the battle.

PACE

I realize that in this chapter we have stressed time "spent" running, not on distance. But just to define "pace", for your information, I'll give you the "numbers", as related by Rory Donaldson and the National Jogging Association in the book, "Guidelines For Successful Jogging."

They say that if you cover one mile in 20 minutes it's a slow walk. A moderate walk is 15 minutes and a fast walk is approximately 13 minutes. One mile covered in 12 minutes is a slow jog, in 10 minutes a moderate jog, in 9 minutes a fast jog. An 8-minute mile is a slow run, a 7-minute mile a moderate run. Below 7 minutes you are, of course, running F-A-S-T.

So there you have it—a plan of action. If after this you yearn for greater challenges, like maybe the Boston Marathon, you'll want to pursue some more advanced programs (and ideas) included in our upcoming chapter, "The Competitive Runner".

Physical Activity Index

Calculate your activity index by multiplying your rating for each activity.

(Index = Intensity x Duration x Frequency):

	Rating	Activity
Intensity	5	Sustained heavy breathing and perspiration
	4	Intermittent heavy breathing and perspiration − as in tennis
	3	Moderately heavy − as in recreational sports and cycling
	2	Moderate − as in volleyball, softball
	1	Light − as in fishing, walking
Duration	4	Over 30 minutes
	3	20 to 30 minutes
	2	10 to 20 minutes
	1	Under 10 minutes
Frequency	5	Daily or almost daily
	4	3 to 5 times a week
	3	1 to 2 times a week
	2	Few times a month
	1	Less than once a month

Evaluation and Fitness Category

Score	Evaluation	Fitness Estimate
100	Very active lifestyle	High
60 to 80	Active and healthy	High
40 to 60	Acceptable (could be better)	Medium
20 to 40	Not good enough	Low
Under 20	Sedentary	Low

8

THE COMPETITIVE RUNNER

Marathon Training Programs

So you want to run in the Boston Marathon? Or maybe one of the other marathons nearest to your home.

This, of course, is a decision that only you can make. As I said in Chapter 8, if you've worked up through my basic Program for six months, you're in condition to enter competition at your own age category.

It could be a real fun thing. There's always plenty of good feelings when runners get together, and most certainly your first marathon would be a challenge, a "happening," and an unforgettable experience.

In this chapter I've put together some programs, and other reflections, that if followed (as you've followed my program up to this point) should put you across the finish line in the marathon of your choice in a few minutes under (or over) three hours—which is kind of a cutting-off point for good runners.

A couple of precautions. Make sure you have completed (without hedging) the programs earlier outlined and that you have your doctor's approval to move up to marathon level. If you are having any problems, such as sore feet, knees, etc., you must take care of them and then decide your course of action. Or it could be that your body's musculature won't, at this point support the added training you need to complete a marathon.

My feeling is that your first marathon should be merely an experiment. In other words, for you it should not really be a competition. You don't want to go all-out, barely staggering across the finish line or having to quit at the 15-mile mark with legs that feel as if they are on fire. You just want to plan carefully and then pace yourself with the idea of finishing no matter how long it takes. And I mean finishing without tearing yourself up either physically or psychologically.

However, I also want to make it clear that by following the training schedule and with certain other hints, there is no reason why your first marathon can't be an exercise in joyful achievement—accomplished in a time that you'll feel proud of.

For starters, I don't think anybody should run more than four marathons a year. Some of the world-class veterans or very experienced runners may be doing it, but even for them, there's a price paid. The body, no doubt about it, needs pushing. But it also needs periods of rest, relaxation, recovery. And remember, marathon running, is one of the most exhausting activities in the world!

Now, following my marathon training program, how long should you train before going to the starting line? I say six months—which means, plus the six-month Basic Program, so the earliest you could run your first marathon if you're a beginning jogger, is one year.

Of course, if you're already running, and in fair shape,

you may want to launch into the marathon program of mine—in your age category—or maybe you've already tried a marathon and are just looking for better methods of approaching another? Here it is!

MARATHON TRAINING PROGRAM: AGES 25-40

If, under-21 (or 18) and over-60 aren't the ages for the marathon as recommended by Bill Emmerton—what are? In my opinion, the "peak" ages are 26-28 years old, and on up, for your top performers.

There are exceptions, but most champion runners in their 30s are beginning to step aside for the younger lions. In 1972, when he won the Olympic Games marathon, Frank Shorter was 25. Derek Clayton of Australia, who set the world record of 2 hours, 8 minutes, and 33 seconds in 1969 was 27 then.

Yet, there's always somebody like Jack Foster of New Zealand, who didn't start running until he was 33, entered competition and was turning in his best times at the age of 41.

But for training purposes, I've put my prime category as 25 to 40 which should include a majority of runners who have the desire and vigor to excel at the distance.

Frank Shorter, claims that for him the sport was 98 per cent training and 2 per cent competition. In one five-year period he was said to have missed only six days of running. Keeping at it, consistency is the key.

Here's our program, to be followed five days a week for six months prior to your first marathon and for three months between marathons. It is designed to give you strength plus speed and put you under 3 hours, which qualifies you for most marathons today.

Monday:	14 miles easy running on road
Tuesday:	6 miles at 85 percent effort on road.
Wednesday:	1 hour, 45 minutes easy running

nonstop on road. Or fast run of 15 miles if you feel like it.

Thursday: 10 miles at 3/4 pace (85 per cent of best effort).

Friday: Rest.

Saturday: 22 miles nonstop on road.

Sunday: Rest.

MARATHON TRAINING PROGRAM: AGES 18-25

There aren't as many runners I've found in this age bracket. But those who do run are fast and energetic, and are on their way toward developing into mature and super marathoners of the 25-40 category. The 18-25s, I believe, can tolerate more work. Their program is the same as 25-40 with a few variations. Thus:

Monday: 16 miles easy running on road.

Tuesday: 8 miles at 85 per cent effort on road.

Wednesday: 15 miles at fast pace on the road.

Thursday: 10 miles to be run between 56 and 57 minutes.

Friday: 8 miles easy running on road.

Saturday: 22 miles easy running nonstop on road.

Sunday: Rest.

Remember, I said that I don't recommend anybody over 60 competing in a marathon. But what about those between 40 and 50? Well, okay, but it's important for them to be getting a little more rest between training runs. So here's a program for them. Of course, if you're right at 60 (or just over) and absolutely insist on running a marathon, this is the schedule for you, too.

And some of the women, who don't quite feel up to the men's schedule for their age group, might be interested in this one.

MARATHON TRAINING PROGRAM: AGES 40-50

Monday:	12 miles easy running on road.
Tuesday:	Rest.
Wednesday:	14 miles easy running on road.
Thursday:	Rest.
Friday:	6 miles easy running on road.
Saturday:	2 hours easy nonstop running on road or grass if you prefer.
Sunday:	Rest.

It's important, especially in this age category, to never exert yourself if you feel tired. It may take you longer to be able to achieve a satisfactory training routine, but don't push it. You'll get there in plenty of time. Also, keep closer tabs on that blood pressure, the basic pulse rate, and take extra care of the joints: knee, hip, and ankle.

In addition to some stretching before and after your run (Chapter 13: Exercise and Running), or even in place of them, a good idea is a massage followed by a hot bath. You can either massage yourself (especially those joints!) or teach your wife . . . husband . . . to help. A time-saver, and real joy, is to massage as you savor that hot tub of water.

You'd be surprised how many leg ailments, etc. can be prevented, by allowing some time to take care of yourself. It's critical when you get past 40. I know, it's one of my secrets to longevity as an ultra-marathon man.

Speaking of the "ultra," how about a program for some of you who might want to extend into some of those runs above and beyond 26 miles, 385 yards? Like maybe, an occasional 50-miler? Here, time spent rather than distance covered is the priority.

You want to get used to the idea of being out on the road from 5½ to 8½ hours on race day.

ULTRA-MARATHON TRAINING PROGRAM: ALL AGES

Monday:	16 miles easy running on road.
Tuesday:	10 miles easy running on road at 7½ minute per mile pace.
Wednesday:	2 hours easy running nonstop on road.
Thursday	2 hours easy running nonstop on road. Both Wednesday and Thursday's suggested pace: 7½ minute.
Friday:	Rest.
Saturday:	25 miles easy running on road.
Sunday:	Rest.

LSD-INTERVAL-FARTLEK

I purposely avoided usage of the term "LSD"—meaning "long slow distance," (not a drug)—during our training programs because there is some confusion in the usage of this terminology. I'm sure it's just a matter of semantics, because my training runs certainly have a lot of "long slow distance" involved. But to me, LSD implies a sort of a leisurely jog—a fun run in the countryside for three or four miles, an hour faster than a walk (of 3 or 4 m.p.h.)

There are a couple of other training-type terms you should be aware of: interval training and fartlek. Interval work consists of repeated hard runs over a definite distance, say on a track, with definite durations of walks or jogs in between the runs. Let's say 220 yards five times at speeds of 30 seconds, interspersed with one-minute walks. You can, of course, pick up the speed and increase the number of times, and/or vary the walking-rest time-period. Before launching into interval work you should be in good shape via longer and slower running, and be careful that you are fully warmed up.

In addition to interval training, most of the great runners

of history—(especially Europeans) employ "fartlek," which is Swedish for "speed play." In it, you perform a series of fast, untimed runs over a variety of terrains and distances. It avoids the monotony and repetition of interval work, but it, too, is hard work. Yet, it can be fun with its spirit of play. I've returned from interval workouts almost exhausted, but felt refreshed after doing fartlek running.

SHORT RUNS

Now, let's say you're just not a marathon type. It's a bit too grueling, time-consuming, whatever. But you would like to compete in other meets of shorter runs, now being held throughout the country.

As with marathon races, you can keep tabs on where and when the competitions are held through the newspapers, or perhaps one of the fine magazines on running now being published, such as Runner's World. The Amateur Athletic Union in your area is a source, or maybe the high school, college athletic department, a sporting goods store. Senior Sports International, sponsor of the annual Senior Olympics, is located on Wilshire Boulevard in Los Angeles.

SPRINTS

If you are also interested in sprints, here are three-month programs for ages 18-35 and 35-50 which—following the six-month Basic Program of Chapter 7—will enable you to race with hopes of glory at anywhere from 3 to 10 miles.

3-TO-10-MILE TRAINING PROGRAM: AGES 18-35

FIRST MONTH

Monday: 10 miles easy running on road, golf course, park.

Tuesday: 8 miles easy running; same (as above) or a varied location.

Wednesday: 12 miles easy running. Location of choice.

Thursday: 5 miles easy running.

Friday: Rest.

Saturday: 12 miles easy running.

Sunday: Rest.

SECOND MONTH

Monday: 10 miles at 3/4 pace on grass, road.

Tuesday: 1 mile jog to warm up.
Track running, 12 x 400 yards repetition running at 3/4 pace; jog 440 yards in between slowly.
5 minutes rest.
12 x 220 yards repetition running at 33-second pace; jog 220 yards in between slowly.
1-½ miles slow jog to warm down.

Wednesday: 1 mile warm up jog on flat ground.
Hill running (find a hill 300 to 400 yards long), 40 minutes, running up the hill, jogging back down until completion of time period.
Warming down exercises.

Thursday: 12 miles easy over-the-distance run.

Friday: 70 minutes of fartlek running; fast repeats of about 50, 100 and 300 yards interspersed with short

"resting" jogs.
Warming down exercises.

Saturday: 12 miles easy over-the-distance run.
Sunday: Rest.

THIRD MONTH

Monday: 10 minutes jogging to warm up.
4 miles non-stop running at hard pace.
1 mile jog to warm down.

Tuesday: 1 mile jog to warm up.
7 miles non-stop running at 3/4 pace.
Warming down exercises.

Wednesday: 1 hour fartlek running; spurts of 50 yards and sprints of 600 yards interspersed with short "resting" jogs.
Warming down exercises.

Thursday: 10 miles very easy running.
Friday: Rest.
Saturday: In morning, 5 miles easy running.
In afternoon, 10 miles running at hard pace.
Warming down exercises.
Sunday: Rest.

You're ready to race!

3-TO-10-MILE TRAINING PROGRAM: AGES 35-50

FIRST MONTH

Monday: 4 Miles steady running on road, golf course park.
Tuesday: 8 miles steady running; location of

your choice.

Wednesday:	6 miles steady running; a good idea is to vary where you run.
Thursday:	1 hours steady running.
Friday:	Rest.
Saturday:	10 miles steady running.
Sunday:	Rest.

SECOND MONTH

Monday:	6 miles running at 3/4 pace.
Tuesday:	½-mile jog to warm up. Track running, 8 x 440 yards running; jog 880 yards (½ mile) in between slowly. 5 minutes rest. 4 x 220 yards repetition running at 3/4 pace; jog 220 yards in between slowly. Warming down exercises.
Wednesday:	6 miles easy running; location of your choice.
Thursday:	1 hour steady running.
Friday:	Rest.
Saturday:	10 miles steady running.
Sunday:	Rest.

THIRD MONTH

Monday:	7 miles easy running.
Tuesday:	45 minutes of fartlek running, fast, slow repeats from 50 to 440 yards. Warming down exercises.
Wednesday:	50 minutes of very easy non-stop running.
Thursday:	½ mile jog to warm up. Hill running (find a hill 300 to 400 yards long), 45 minutes, running up the hill, jogging back down until

	completion of time period.
Friday:	Rest.
Saturday:	12 miles very easy running.
Sunday:	Rest.

You're ready to race!

ADDITIONAL TIPS

As you already know, before any race, or workout, you should not overload the digestive system. A cup of tea or warm soup is sufficient. And you shouldn't eat afterwards for a couple of hours. Especially at a marathon, you may only wish fluids for several hours afterwards.

The day before a race like a marathon, eat normally but cut the intake by half. Eat a light breakfast (say, tea, poached egg, whole wheat toast) a couple of hours before the start of the race.

As I said, you need a year's training to be ready for a marathon race and your first one should be experimental. I'm also a believer that you should work out at the marathon distance three or four times before entering one. This gives you more confidence and a chance to work out some of the problems that might hang-up your performance.

What about pace, strategy for your marathon run? I think your first 10 miles should be slower; the average runner gets carried away with the excitement and goes too fast too early. You should run evenly (though not TOO slowly) the first 10; never under 67 minutes if you're aiming to break three hours.

You might pick up the pace a bit then, if you're feeling good. But, in general, I think the first 20 miles should be run at an even, comfortable pace. Then, if you've trained well, while others are "hitting that wall" at 20 miles, you can pick up your speed and actually reduce your time by six to seven minutes the last 6 miles, 385 yards.

So good luck in your marathon (or shorter) runs.

9

THE WOMAN RUNNER

Enjoying A New Life Style

Along the Pacific Ocean at Santa Monica there is a nature strip long used by joggers. It is from beginning to end about 10 miles, and I've used it for years to add variety to my workouts. One afternoon not long ago, I drove by and true to tradition, my running friends were there, and the "majority" of joggers were women.

What we're seeing today—this very year, in fact—is a mass breakthrough of women into running. No longer are women concerned about the old "weaker sex" labels. In fact, there is mounting evidence that in many categories important to successful running, women are actually the "stronger sex."

When I first came to the United States, I must admit that I was shocked at the poor fitness level of many American women. In my home country of Australia, and in Europe where I'd traveled, women ran, swam, bicycled, or at the least walked . . . if only because there were not as many automobiles.

Now that so many American women have gotten into the newer life styles, I fully expect them to surpass any achievements by their across-the-ocean-counterparts.

This is already becoming evident in the longer distances, where women in their 20s, 30s and 40s are challenging marathon records, like 42-year-old Japan born Miki Gorman, who has won ten 26-milers, including twice at Boston; 23-year-old Kim Merritt of Wisconsin, the American record-holder (2 hours, 37 minutes, 58 seconds); and Jackie Hanson of California who formerly held the world record.

By 1984 the hope is that the women's marathon race will be added to the Olympic Games program—a step forward that would have been considered impossible a decade ago.

Women weren't supposed to be able to go much beyond a mile. Now women like Eileen Waters and Donna Gookin of San Diego are recording marks at 50-plus-miles, while in South Africa, Mavis Hutchinson is making like Bill Emmerton with her city-to-city ultra runs.

Now that running, or jogging, has become a "thing," or "happening," for many women in America, from these growing numbers will come many of the world's future champions.

THE NEW WOMAN

You speak of your Super Woman on television. Do you want my forecast of who the REAL Super Woman of the future will be? It's the young woman—perhaps not yet into serious, or any, running—who becomes the first of her sex to run the four-minute mile.

In fact, I'm going to startle a few purists by predicting that during the next 10 years we'll see (1) a four-minute mile by a woman, (2) a two-hour, 20-minute marathon by a woman, and (3) a 50-mile run in under six hours, by a woman.

Of course, these super achievements must be viewed as the tip of the iceberg. What we're really talking about, as women get into jogging (as well as other endeavors), is a vast sociological revolution that affects a way of life, relationships, and a variety of other issues, not to mention health.

Many women have cast aside old ways of thinking. Instead of standing on the sidelines cheering for the man, or waiting patiently for him to return home after HIS workout, she's jogging (and getting fit) herself . . . either by herself or with him. Instead of viewing perspiration as being "unfeminine" she's out there sweating with the best of them. Instead of fearing being scoffed at as she trudges along in the initial stages, she's with the many, who may soon be outnumbering the bystanders.

The basis for all this increasing participation in my opinion, is a woman's instinctive enthusiasm and concern. She's constantly informed by the magazines, newspapers, and television shows about physical fitness through jogging. Also, I think, there's a search for and discovery of a greater identity.

I have talked with many women who just did not feel well, until they got into jogging. They had headaches. They tired easily. They felt stress at work, unfulfilled, burdened at home. A doctor could write a prescription, perhaps; but that help was usually temporary. In a nutshell, these women weren't really aware of - or - in touch with—their body's capabilities. And one survey, sadly enough, revealed that the least fit of any segment of the American population was the woman aged 20-29, surely a prime time of life.

A friend of mine, a San Francisco physician, Dr. Joan Ullyot, has written a book, "Women's Running", because she was also a victim of the feeling-rotten syndrome. One day, as she sat in Golden Gate Park watching her husband run, it occurred to her that she, too, could run . . . though "I'd never seen a woman running. The whole concept was foreign to me." She has since competed in marathons and is a leading spokeswoman for the jogging movement.

You can develop a list six miles long, I'm sure, of women who now enjoy a new feeling of well-being through jogging; how (with proper food intake) they've been able to lose weight; how their sex life has improved; how various parts of their body have been toned, firmed; how they have achieved a glowing self-esteem; and how they are better able to cope with stress situations.

Women I've consulted say that both their pulse rate and blood pressure have been lowered—just as with men. And they report weight loss particularly in the regions of the hips and thighs. Plus an overall firming up of muscles throughout the body.

HEALTH

An article in Playboy magazine a while back stated that jogging could be hazardous—that the activity can displace the uterus and cause the breasts to sag, by snapping ligaments. Actually, the breasts are firmed because of the arm action in jogging that helps to strengthen the pectoral muscles. Also, I've never heard of any women having problems with the uterus because of running. And I've talked to many doctor friends of mine about it.

Incidentally, I'm often asked: "Should I wear a bra when jogging?" My answer is that it's probably better if you do, though it's not absolutely necessary. Whatever suits your comfort. Also, it depends on the size of your bust whether a bra is especially advisable.

What about menstruation? Some people say it's wise to skip exercise during those days because it's uncomfortable to run with cramps. However, many women continue to jog during their period, claiming the run cuts down on the acuteness of the cramps. Also, the runners in good physical condition have fewer premenstral tensions, they say.

Studies I've read say there's little difference in the ability to run well, whether you're in or out of the menstrual cycle. In fact, a group of competitors in all phases of their "life cycle" were studied at the 1964 Olympics at Tokyo. The result:

it didn't much matter. Performances were both good (medal-winning) and bad in all phases. What mattered, of course, was the usual: conditioning, confidence, and ability.

Pregnancy is another female concern. Do you quit, and at what point? Many women continue to run up until six weeks before the due date. However, if you wish to play it a bit safer, you might consider (besides, of course, quitting altogether) jogging the first six months of your pregnancy and walking briskly the last three. In any event, you should consult your doctor for advise.

Women who have been running until or during pregnancy tell me that they were better able to handle the childbirth itself—it being less painful and not as exhausting—plus they had far better stamina soon afterwards. And they had no trouble returning to their running at the same level as before.

BODY RESPONSES

Right now the women marathoners are running about 20 per cent slower than the best men. This is understandable, since women have a smaller heart size and lesser oxygen-carrying capacity than men—plus the fact that they are not usually as strong in the matter of muscles, tendons, ligaments, etc.

Yet, the best women marathon runners are already outdistancing two-thirds of the male competitors. And I think the day is coming when the best women will outperform the best men at the ultra-distances of 50 miles and up.

Women are able to run better than men (or will be, given training over distances) because, in the first place, their muscle amounts to only 23 per cent of the body while with men it's 40 per cent. Thus, women have more fat tissue and this is the source for energy over a long period of time. They simply have greater potential stamina, especially in long runs.

Some people have commented that many women run awkwardly. This may be the case for some who have a weight problem or who haven't used their running muscles for years. But my impression is that many women have a grace (if not power) that men lack. And, indeed, their movement has been shown to be more economical than men's. A study at Penn State conducted by Dr. Richard Nelson and Christine Brooks showed that women took more steps per minute, contacted the ground less, and had bigger strides in accordance with their height.

I have noticed that women actually seem to suffer fewer strains and blisters than men, and definitely they are less stiff after a marathon. However, many have a tendency to have achilles tendon problems, because they're used to wearing high heel shoes; quite a few have to be educated not to run so much on their toes; and because their joints are looser, the knees may be slightly more prone to injury.

Many possible strains can be averted by a proper getting-into-it-slowly approach and good equipment—particularly the shoes. As we mentioned in Chapter 3, the shoe manufacturers finally have come out with new lines of comfortable, superior and protective women's footwear.

With the shoes has come new and fashionable running gear. I look forward to seeing jogging suits (or track outfits) that women wear, as carefully designed as made-to-order-gowns, and much more popular.

It used to be, also, that the women "tagged along" in the men's marathons. Remember Kathy Switzer and her Boston Marathon episode in the late 1960s. Now women not only have a whole series of national and international marathons, but there are mini-marathons (perhaps 6 and 10-mile runs) with huge sponsership by major companies. Many events now attract thousands—from pre-teens to women in their 50s and 60s. Every woman runs! Or have you already forgotten our 80-year-old Eula Weaver who's a champion in her age bracket?

THE NEW FEELING

With more women now running, it puts them on a common ground with their husbands . . . providing the husband runs, too. And, if not, she might even inspire him!

There is no better time to talk things out, I've found, than when jogging at a comfortable pace with someone you are close to. I'm less tense then. My thoughts flow more freely. I'm more direct, perhaps more honest. I just feel like talking . . . or listening, as the case may be. Many women have told me that for them, running is another expression of "feeling."

So, in my opinion, running opens tremendous doors of communication. Of course, one or the other partner may have to slow down to tailor his (or her) pace to the other. But this shouldn't be too difficult. Family jogging has also come of age. It, of course, requires a commitment and even though you're in a group, you're still individually jogging and benefitting.

There have been women who, extremely serious about their running, have somewhat "neglected" the man in their life, consequently creating difficulties in their relationship. This is the old "golf widow" syndrome in reverse.

My answer to this is that such a woman should do everything she can to get her husband (friend) to jog (or walk) with her, at least some of the time. A fit woman is too valuable to herself, not to mention to the family unit, to be giving up her best-of-health. With it, she's also a positive influence on the children (who'll of course become joggers).

Arthur Lydiard, the famous Olympic coach from New Zealand summed it up, "Women can train as long as men can train, can run as far as men can run, they can do it seven days a week all year through. A few years ago, people would have considered this either impossible or unwise."

10

FOOD AND THE RUNNER

Just What To Eat

One of my favorite marathon-race stories concerns Felix Carvajal, a Cuban mailman who ran in the very early Olympic Games. Carvajal, it seems, not only had never before completed the 20-mile-plus distance, but as he got hungry during the race, he began eating apples and peaches that he picked from trees along the way.

You guessed it: our runner got one big stomach ache and had to lie down beside the road to rest. After a while, he started running again and finished a respectable (surprising) fourth.

I bring up free-spirited Felix because he is almost the antithesis of today's "scientific" runner with his miracle foods and nutritional strategies designed to help him (or her) to bigger and better training and competition efforts.

Of course, nobody should eat while involved in an exhaustive exercise such as a marathon—everybody knows that. You want to keep the body well supplied with fluids. You want to be in super cardiovascular and skeletal condition. And you want to eat properly BEFORE, AFTER, AND APPROACHING competition.

I must say right off the top that I'm not a nutritionist. If you want to get the "bookish viewpoint", there are many references on the subject. What I am offering are some tips, and a daily "menu" of living that has helped me maintain maximum health and good running form for many years and many miles.

In my lectures, I've often been asked, "Bill, which is more important—food or exercise—in sustaining good health?" There's an implication here, of course, that you can pay more attention to one than the other.

It is difficult to answer this question because I believe both are extremely important. One, really, aids and compliments the other. It's the old story of the cart and the horse. I personally like the horse AND the cart. But, if I can draw a parallel, I'd say for me the horse represents exercise (of a vigorous nature) and the cart is food. Not wishing to put the cart before the horse, I have to lean towards exercise as being somewhat more important.

What maximum health really is, in my opinion, is feeding all parts of the body via a bloodstream that is pulsating with nutrients and oxygen, which reaches every cell, that makes up every tissue that, in turn, makes up each and every organ.

With a strong heart that pumps the blood efficiently, and "fit" and clear arteries, the food that you eat builds, maintains, and protects the body from disease. It also provides energy to keep the "engine" running—that is to say, the heart, lungs, kidneys, liver, muscles, brain, the works.

Unless you are eating a diet completely lacking in nutrition, and most people today aren't, exercise is the more important of our disciplines because the super-vigorous body at least gets whatever food value you DO consume to the right places. An unfit, a sluggish, a "clogged up" system can't properly feed, no matter how superior the foods.

DIET

I certainly don't consider myself as any kind of a food "faddist," and I can adapt my eating to almost any sort of circumstance. But I do greatly enjoy eating at home, and when there, I try to follow a diet known to have plenty of LIFE PRINCIPLE. In other words, if it's alive, if it's not (too) denatured—that's my kind of food. This includes, of course, fresh fruits and vegetables, dairy products, eggs, some meats and especially fish and chicken, that are low in saturated fat.

Implied in what you do eat is what you DON'T eat; and when and how much. Everybody, including myself, eats food that we have come to enjoy and rely upon for taste, convenience, and performance.

As a general rule, I think people eat too much—and that includes bad as well as good food. Psychologists will give you reasons for excessive eating, but my experience has been that if you are a happy and productive person—and particularly one that is running regularly—you won't require food as an outlet.

After they have "sinned" by overeating and looking and feeling it, many people want to go on one of those so-called crash diets. This is about the worst thing that you can do because it not only takes away your energy but it weakens the heart as well as other muscles.

Steady exercise and good nutritious dieting is the way to drop off pounds, in my opinion. And it should be done very gradually, to allow the body time to adjust. If you are 50 pounds overweight, you shouldn't expect to take it off in six months; better to allow one year or longer. After all, your total health—not just whether you look trim and fit—is the issue at stake.

Regularity, then, is crucial to keeping the body in top condition as far as I'm concerned—regularity in running, in exercising, in eating, in all the other big and small habits a person retains for one reason or another.

STARTING THE DAY

With regularity in mind, let's go through a day in the life of Bill Emmerton—ultra-long-distance-jogger, exponent of total fitness via the CORRECT way to live. We'll take a few detours and my way might not fit exactly into your schedule or life-style, but I am certain that there will be some very worth-while ideas for you to use.

Buzzzzzz! (or ringgggg!). What's that? It sounds like my alarm clock has just gone off. Time to leap (I mean get) out of bed...after, of course, another night of refreshing sleep, the kind you get if you are running regularly. I am usually up by 7:00, and I always try to get somewhere between six and eight hours of sleep.

After a quick trip to the bathroom, I head for the kitchen, where the day starts with a cup of hot water mixed with a teaspoonful of honey and the juice of a lemon. There is, I believe, nothing better for the body than a clean digestive system.

After my morning constitutional, I'm ready to get my body moving with a little exercise. I'm not a believer in vigorous exercise early-on, unless you just can't fit your run in at another time. I like to start with a few standing knee-lifts. Just stand erect, raise the leg about waist-high (or higher) by bending the knee, then place the foot on the floor and do the same with the other leg. I do a dozen knee-lifts with each leg, but you might start with, four or a half-dozen and work your way up to a number (even more than a dozen) that's comfortable for you. The knee-lifts are good for the legs and joints, of course, but I believe they also help the digestive tract as well.

The body is at its lowest resistance point early in the morning and I'm a believer in taking your time to get going. Too many people, in my opinion, jump out of bed, dress in a frenzy, gulp down a cup of coffee, and rush off to work. Or, if not quite as frenetic, they still aren't taking the time to ease into the day.

By rushing too early, you are tensing the muscles and depriving your system of much-needed oxygen. This hurry-up-I've-got-to-get-to-work way of living, in my opinion, is a real killer. If you must get to work early, give yourself time by going to bed earlier and getting up earlier.

After a shower and dressing, I'm ready for my breakfast —which I think is the most important meal of the day. Why? Because in breaking your night's "fast" you are feeding the body with the nutrients that it will need for energy the remainder of the day. Other foods will "build" on the foundation you establish at breakfast.

As indicated, you don't want one of those coffee-and-rolls breakfasts, which lack nutrition, but neither do you want to stuff yourself with a huge breakfast.

I like, for breakfast, some fresh (or frozen) fruit, perhaps followed by oatmeal sprinkled with wheat germ and raisins, and of course milk. Nutrition is important, but so is variety. You know, the old spice of life!

An alternate breakfast might be an "orange nog." Fresh orange juice blended with honey, an egg (whole), wheat germ, gelatin, and a dash of nutmeg. A dish of yogurt topped with fresh fruit follows, and perhaps some whole wheat toast.

A third alternate is a blended drink of prune juice, the juice of a lemon, a banana, and yogurt, followed by some poached eggs (one or two) on whole wheat toast. You might start this one off with fresh fruit—such as, a half a grapefuit.

I personally believe that liquids, such as tea or coffee, should be taken either before or maybe a half-hour (or longer) after a meal. It's better for your (at least for my) digestion.

LUNCH

The first meal having been consumed, it's time to get into the day—your job, other matters (or joys!) around the home.

What about vitamins? I take them, yes, but in mid-morning, about 10:30; vitamins C and E and a multiple capsule. Vitamin C, I believe, helps in a variety of repair and disease-prevention functions. And "E," could help increase stamina and endurance by getting oxygen to the blood.

For my lunch, I like some fresh fruit, a vegetable, and pro-tein—perhaps fish or poultry. Or maybe a fruit salad plate: bed of crisp lettuce, cottage cheese, topped by a jello mold. And a slice of pumpernickel or raisin bread. Or a shrimp omelete over chopped spinach, with whole wheat toast. These dishes are often preceded by a pineapple punch (the juice mixed with honey and yogurt or milk) or hot tomato zip (the juice mixed with honey, lemon juice, and Worcester-shire sauce).

Anyway, lunch should be light and nutritious. In fact, I'm inclined to believe that you should eat four times a day—it being easier on your digestive system to handle smaller quantities of food at a sitting. So, with a very light lunch, and perhaps a couple of hours before your late-afternoon (or early evening) run, a snack of tea or coffee, whole wheat toast or muffin should be enough to keep you until dinner.

Time, again, should be taken to savor your time-period of working out. Dress slowly and carefully. Massage, stretch before. Afterwards, massage, stretch. Get into a hot tub (not shower unless that's your preference or all that's available). Relax before your evening meal.

DINNER

I'm a firm believer in a light dinner—and one that's eaten at least two or three hours before you retire to bed. The body, is now beginning to slow down and is not prepared to handle a big meal, as many people insist on having. Also, you tend to sleep better on a less-than-full stomach. And sleep is that important time when the body heals, or knits itself.

Throughout the day, my objective is to get in the four basic types of food: (1) fruits and vegetables; (2) cereals; (3) protein (meat, eggs); and (4) some dairy. All of course, of the life-principle variety.

I want, maybe, three different fruits and a trio of fresh (cooked) vegetables. Since I'm getting fruit earlier in the day, I usually look forward to vegetables at dinner. Here are a couple of examples of dinners conceived (and prepared) by my wife:

—Light Chicken Dinner ... Starts with cranberry creme appetizer (chilled cranberry juice and yogurt), followed by baked breast of chicken garnished with wheat germ and parsley bits. Some steamed spinach, and vegetable rice (brown) with chopped green peppers, celery, mushrooms, sunflower seeds, and cooked peas. Fresh fruit for desert is optional.

—Salmon Loaf Dinner ... Starts with tomato cocktail (tomato juice, dash of lemon juice, curry powder), followed by baked salmon loaf prepared with wheat germ and chopped green peppers and parsley, served with steamed broccoli and Mexican-style corn.

After dinner, it's not a bad idea, in my opinion, to take a slow walk for about 10 minutes. And then just relax: reading, a show or movie, television, conversation. Soon, if you've done your working out, you'll be ready for the joy of bed and a sound sleep.

CARBOHYDRATE DIETS

One of the diets I feel it is important to comment on is the recent advent of carbohydrate loading for runners who compete in marathons. I am opposed to this six-day diet, in which the runner eats a high-protein, high-fat diet for the first three days to rid the body of excess glycogen.

Then, during the next three days, just before the race, most fats and protein are avoided and the body is fed large amounts of carbohydrates—like spaghetti, bread, pizza, cake, ice cream—to build up stores of the most easily-converted fuel, glycogen ... from the carbohydrates.

The idea is that you will have more energy during the race, particularly at about the 20-mile mark (known as "hitting the wall") when the energy stores are pretty well depleted. The added glycogen, providing more than the normal exercise tolerance, supposedly gives you that added kick.

Of course, if continued, such a diet could harm one's health, since the body needs fats and proteins. In my opinion, this "overloading" has been emphasized beyond its importance. If anything, the body should go through a "cleansing" by cutting the normal food intake by one-half during the pre-race final 24 hours.

How well you run will be mostly determined by how fit you are, if you race intelligently, so as not to speed too soon (thus harming your ability to finish), and whether you utilize fluids to the utmost of your capacity. Never, of course, eat just before or during a race—or have you forgotten our Cuban friend Felix Carvajal and his marathon stomach ache?

	Calories per minute*	Time taken to burn approx. 200 calories (in minutes)
Calisthenics	5.0	40
Walking (3½ mph)	5.6	36
Cycling (10 mph)	8.5	24
Swimming (crawl)	9.0	22
Skipping Rope (120/min)	10.0	20
Jogging (5 mph)	10.0	20
Running (7.5 mph)	15.0	14

*Exact calories burned depends on efficiency and body size.

11

RUNNING AND OTHER SPORTS

Improving Your Game

By now I can hear you thinking out loud:

Well, running may be the greatest sport in the world (it is, it is!) but what about those other sports I enjoy?

Do I have to put away my tennis racquet? What about that bowling date I have on Wednesday night? And if I'm training for the marathon, won't I be too tired for my favorite game, golf?

I'll have to admit, it's been a good many years since I've been involved in any other sports. But at one point in my youth, I was the Tazmanian boxing champion. I never lost an amateur fight but I did get beat up enough while winning to realize that it wasn't my game.

I played some Australian Rules football, and have played golf and coached at tennis. But largely since my 20s, I have devoted my energies to running—first as one of the top amateurs in Australia and then later as a professional.

Turning pro ended any hopes I had for Olympic Game glory. But I did win more than 150 amateur championships, ranging from the half-mile to the marathon, and I also represented my country in international competition. At one stage, my time at 5,000 meters was one of the half-dozen best in the world.

I don't think anybody should have to give up a sport that he or she truly enjoys playing—just as you should not have to quit watching television, going to the theater, or doing whatever turns you on.

But I want to make some basic points in this chapter, and the first is that all sports—practically without exception —should be regarded for what they are: pastimes of entertainment and enjoyment. . .not mostly exercise.

At least not exercise that affords to you the total and long-lived potential benefits of jogging or more serious running. Or, for that matter, plain old walking. That's right—what you do when you head down to the corner store: walk! I hope you haven't become such a victim of the "automobile culture" that you can no longer find the time or energy to walk short distances when the opportunity occurs.

There are some sports that are skill types—such as golf, bowling, tennis, baseball—but which neither require nor return fitness, as I define the word.

Gymnastics certainly is good for the skeletal muscles and flexibility. Swimming is an excellent exercise for most of the body's muscles, including the heart. And bicycling, too, is excellent cardiovascularly, though it (besides the heart) only aids the legs. Skiing (cross country) is also a very good exercise.

QUICK START/STOP SPORTS

In the past ten years, tennis has become a tremendously popular sport and following in it's wake are other sports:

racquet ball, handball, squash, other quick-start-and-stop challenges.

I don't suppose I'll make any friends with the tennis set by saying that I think it's potentially dangerous to your health, unless you are totally fit for it. And that goes for the other quick-start, racquet-type games, too.

In the chapter on "Running for Longevity" we'll go into matters of the heart and what's known as the "training effect." In my opinion, many people who suddenly go out in the hot sun and start chasing a ball back and forth are risking the possibility of harm.

In the first place, if knees, joints, muscles, etc. aren't prepared, the player could readily injure them. Then, if the heart is thrown into sudden over-exertion, a strain (or attack) could be the result. The over-arm action in the tennis serve could also pull a chest muscle, or repture a heart segment.

These possibilities are especially true for people over 40 who play on weekends. The so-called (weekend) "social sportsman" who tends to be overweight and enjoys a nip or two at the bar, along with his "exercise," is particularly vulnerable. Alcohol (like cigarettes) elevates the blood pressure and pulse un-naturally.

Before alienating anybody further, I want to make it clear that I don't consider other sports completely lacking in fitness benefits. Many, burn plenty of calories (though not as many as running) and rate well in the categories of endurance, strength, balance and flexibility— not to mention sleep-inducing and just plain fun.

But they don't improve the crucial areas of heart and lungs by their duration and intensity of exertion. And this is what is most needed. I think Dr. Ken Cooper in his book "Aerobics" says it well, talking about the aerobics benefit of tennis (and handball):

"You dash about the court chasing the ball, and the heart rate goes up to 150 or more. A point is scored and the action stops. The heart rate comes down to 120 or less. After a few games like this, the average heart rate is less than the 150 produced by nonstop aerobics (such as running). There is a definite aerobic benefit, but the point value levels out somewhere between running and walking."

GETTING THE EDGE

In America, the sad irony is that many of your highly-paid professional athletes are so unfit on the scale of "endurance" that they'd be put to shame by any fairly good marathon runner. I'm speaking primarily about football, baseball, and golf—though it extends by degrees into other sports.

It came as no surprise to me that South Africa's Gary Player rallied in the final round to win this year's Masters Golf Tournament in Augusta, Ga. He's a man who exercises (yes, running plus others) religiously—something a lot of the others on tour don't do. I really believe that the extra advantage he had was the endurance to play his best under pressure, when the others were tiring towards the end.

In fact, I firmly believe that once a top athlete has developed his playing skills, and can keep up efficient timing, he'd do best to jog, say in the evening, rather than spend that hour every day hitting buckets of golf balls, batting baseballs, or tennis balls.

Not only would he play better in the final stages of the game, when it's often won or lost, but he'd probably prolong his career. There's no reason, in my opinion, why most athletes can't maintain their proficiency well into their 40s—if they work at it.

A good deal of the problem, I think, is the coaching in this country. The coaches here don't seem to drive their athletes to the point of exhaustion. I personally like somebody, such as the legendary Vince Lombardi, coach of the Green Bay Packers, who was committed totally to victory. And I just love that quote he's famous for:

"Fatique makes cowards of us all."

Isn't that great? And so true!

Percy Cerutty was a lot like Lombardi. Many Australians thought he was a "madman." But old Percy (who I'm certain considered himself part genius) didn't care. He just went about his business of running, step by step, lifting pound for pound, exhorting, cajoling, teaching, preaching, and turning his athletes into world champions.

Percy's game, in my opinion, was motivation. He'd do anything you could, and sometimes more. It was he who convinced me that I should try those cross-country, city-to-city 100-mile runs.

The night before his most famous pupil, Herb Elliott, was to run the Olympics 1,500 meters at Rome, Cerutty slipped a note under Herb's door. It read: "I've just thrashed my body unmercifully for 20 miles. Now it's your turn. Surely you can do the same for 1,500 meters, which is 120 yards short of a mile."

Now, I ask, who wouldn't give all you've got for a coach (and friend) like that? Elliott, made a mockery of his opponents that day, winning by some 20 yards.

So, what do you, who like your sports do, now that you also want excellent fitness?

First, I'd get down to basics—such as the Basic Program offered in this book's Chapter 8. Then, after I felt I'd really gained enough fitness to be in complete physical control of myself, I'd begin incorporating my sport—or sports—into the off-days I don't work out with my running.

But I'd never start cheating on the basic running program. It's the key to everything I believe in. And even if you get to play your favorite sport less often, you'll enjoy it more—and be better at it because of your newfound conditioning.

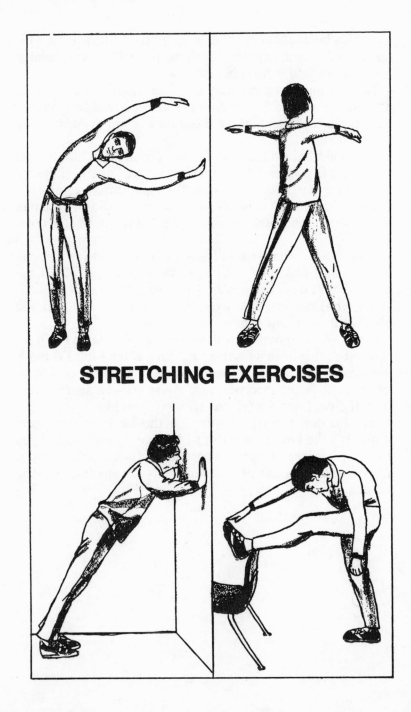

STRETCHING EXERCISES

12

EXERCISE AND RUNNING

Helping Your Body's Performance

When I was a youngster just starting to run, I would jog a 10-mile course across the farmlands of Australia.

One of our neighbors was a 240-pound giant of a fellow in his mid-30s who would tease me about my everyday exercises, as I ran by his portion of my "course."

"That running's going to kill you," he would yell at me. "You ought to eat more. You need more strength. Yo; 're too skinny."

One day my farmer friend called me aside, saying "Come here Bill, I want to show you what real strength is."

He was a muscular man, with large arms, a broad back,

an impressive chest, and legs like tree stumps, though, his large protruding stomach wasn't the picture of health.

He took me into a paddock where he cared for his pigs, walked quickly over to one, took a deep breath and a loud grunt as he picked one pig up about shoulder-high, and then suddenly keeled over—dead.

The poor pig (let along Bill Emmerton) never knew what hit him! It was, of course, a massive heart attack, brought on by exertion to a system not prepared for a sudden shock. I felt terrible about it for a long time, but have since realized that this poor fellow probably would have died soon anyway, he was in such terrible cardiovascular condition.

So, whenever I want to think in terms of which is more important—impressive-looking muscles capable of lifting Porky Pig or a sleek type of machine that can skim off 10 miles in, more-or-less, an hour—I think back to that tragic day.

I'm not against muscles, not even those that ripple right out of the pages of the latest body-building magazine. It's just that I feel those kind of muscles look nice if you're flexing your biceps in the Mr. America contest. And the facts are, that the greater the "mass" of muscle you have in your upper body regions, the harder the heart has to work, and consequently the less chance you have for a long life. It's the guys with skinny shoulders who wouldn't be caught dead at Muscle Beach, who have the best chance to live past 100.

Yet, even with your running program, I think a modest schedule of supplementary weight-lifting is good. The body has 1,030 skeletal muscles, and calisthentics, yoga, stretching, weight routines that can help give these muscles strength and flexibility are an excellent approach to total health.

I have to admit that I'm not nearly as enthusiastic about calisthentics, as I am on running. But I do have some suggestions of routines that have helped me. But if you feel you want to REALLY get into other exercises—perhaps work out your own kind of program to go along with your jogging —it'll certainly do you good.

THE WARMUP

Now for some ideas about non-running exercises.

In the first place, before and after you start your running program, on workout days I believe you should do stretches.

Many of the very best runners, of course, pay special attention to making sure that their legs are in super stretched-out and warmed-up condition before they start a long run. The reasoning is simple. Running is an exercise in specialization, with the legs hitting the ground some 800 times each leg, for each mile covered. And running tends to constrict, or shorten (tighten), the muscles—in the legs as well as the back, and the stomach in particular. Thus, the importance of stretching—which lengthens the muscles.

As important as it is to run, and keep in good stretching form on those days, it's also an important health habit to exercise at all times, throughout your life.

For example, I don't feel it's good to sit around—as in the office at your desk, or in the car, an airplane, wherever—for any extended period of time. The body needs to be fed oxygen, to get circulation, so you should get up and walk around a bit, whenever possible.

Maybe, while you're walking, do a little twisting and stretching, perhaps some deep breathing.

Before conditioning exercises or circulatory activities are attempted, the body should be warmed up to increase respiration and body temperature and to stretch ligaments and connective tissue. The following warmup activities concentrate on stretching the lower back area and therefore contribute to the prevention of lower back problems.

Standing Reach and Bend
Starting Position:
> Stand erect, feet shoulder width apart, arms extended over head.

Action:
> Stretch as high as possible, keeping heels on ground.
>
> Hold for 15 to 30 counts.

Flexed-Leg Back Stretch

Starting Position:

> Stand erect, feet shoulder width apart, arms at side.

Action:

> Slowly bend over, touching the ground between the feet. Keep the knees flexed. Hold for 15 to 30 counts. If at first you can't reach the ground, touch the top of your shoe line.
> Repeat 2 to 3 times.

Alternate Knee Pull

Starting Position:

> Lie on back, feet extended, hands at side.

Action:

> Pull one leg to chest, grasp with both arms and hold for a five count. Repeat with opposite leg.
> Repeat 7-10 times with each leg.

Double Knee Pull

Starting Position:

> Lie on back, feet extended, hands at side.

Action:

> Pull both legs to chest, lock arms around legs, pull buttocks slightly off ground. Hold for 30 to 40 counts.
> Repeat 7-10 times.

Torso Twist

Starting Position:

> Lie on back, knees bent, feet on the ground,* fingers laced behind neck.

Action:

> 1. Curl torso to upright position and twist touching the right knee with the opposite elbow.
> 2. Return to starting position.
> 3. Repeat twisting the opposite direction. Exhale on the way up, inhale on the way down. Repeat 5 to 15 series.

*For best effects secure your feet under something to prevent them from lifting during action.

CONDITIONING EXERCISES

The following exercises are for both men and women and should be considered as a basic all-round series of exercises.

ABDOMINAL
Select the one for you.

Head and Shoulder Curl
Starting Position:
> Lie on back, legs straight, arms at sides.

Action:
> Count 1 -Curl head and shoulders off floor. Hold this position for 5 counts.
>
> Count 2 -Return to starting position.
>
> Suggested repetitions: 10-15

Situp, Arms Crossed (Intermediate)
Starting Position:
> Lie on back, arms crossed on chest, hands grasping opposite shoulders.

Action:
> Count 1 -Curl up to sitting position.
>
> Count 2 -Curl down to starting position.
>
> Suggested repetitions: 10-15

Situp, Fingers Laced (Advanced)
Starting Position:
> Lie on back, legs extended and feet spread one foot apart fingers laced behind neck.

Action:
> Count 1 -Curl up to sitting position and touch right elbow to left knee.
>
> Count 2 -Curl down to sitting position.
>
> Count 3 -Curl up to sitting position and touch left elbow to right knee.

Count 4 -Curl down to starting position.
Suggested repetitions: 15-25

SHOULDER-ARM

Horizontal Arm Circles
Starting Position:
Stand erect, arms extended sideways at shoulder height, palms up.
Action:
Describe small circles backward with hands and arms. Reverse, turn palms down and do small circles forward.
Suggested repetitions: 15-20

Giant Arm Circles
Starting Position:
Stand erect, feet shoulder width apart, arms at sides.
Action:
Bring arms upward and sideways, crossing overhead, completing a full arc in front of body.
Do equal number in each direction.
Suggested repetitions: 10

ARMS AND CHEST

When doing these exercises, keeping the back straight is important. Start with the knee pushup and continue for several weeks until your stomach muscles are toned up enough to keep your back straight. Then try the intermediate.

Knee Pushup (Beginner)
Starting Position:
Lie prone, hands outside shoulders, fingers pointing forward, knees bent.
Action:
Count 1 -Straighten arms, keeping back straight.
Count 2 -Return to starting position.
Suggested repetitions: 5-10

Pushup (Intermediate)

Starting Position:
>Lie prone, hands outside shoulders, fingers pointing forward, feet on floor.

Action:
>Count 1 -Straighten arms, keeping back straight.
>Count 2 -Return to starting position.
>Suggested repetitions: 10-20

Pushup Betwen Chairs (Advanced)

Starting Position:
>Support body on hands on edges of chairs placed slightly outside of shoulders, fingers pointing forward. Body should be straight, with feet resting on chair.

Action:
>Count 1 -Lower body as far as possible, bending elbows.
>Count 2 -Push body up to starting position.
>Suggested repetitions: 5-10

LOWER BODY

This sequence of exercises is designed to tone up your thighs, buttocks and calves. Do each of them with every workout.

Quarter Knee Bends

Starting Position:
>Stand erect, hands on hips, feet comfortably spaced.

Action:
>Count 1 -Bend knees to 45 degrees, keeping heels on floor.
>Count 2 -Return to starting position.
>Suggested repetitions: 15-20

Sitting Single Leg Raises

Starting Position:
>Sit erect, hands on side of chair seat for balance.

Legs extended at angle to floor.

Action:

Count 1 -Raise left leg waist high.
Count 2 -Return to starting position.
Repeat equal number with opposite leg.
Suggested repetitions: 10-15

Side Lying Leg Lift

Starting Position:

Lie on right side, leg extended.

Action:

Count 1 -Raise left leg as high as possible.
Count 2 -Lower to starting position.
Repeat on opposite side.
Suggested repetitions: 10-15

Back Leg Swing

Starting Position:

Stand erect behind chair, feet together, hands on chair for support.

Action:

Count 1 -Lift one leg back and up as far as possible.
Count 2 -Return to starting position.
Repeat equal number of times with other leg.
Suggested repetitions: 20

Heel Raises

Starting Position:

Stand erect, hands on hips, feet together

Action:

Count 1 -Raise body on toes.
Count 2 -Return to starting position.
Suggested repetitions: 20

WEIGHT LIFTING

At home, or perhaps in a gymnasium of your choice, it might be wise to work with weights and do some calisthentics and/or yoga on the days that you aren't running. Some people I know, have their own little "gymnasium" or special area that they set aside to work-out in their home.

A little music to put you in a receptive mood can be a big help. If you're exercising at home, a good investment is a slant board. There are some good weight-lifting exercises that can be performed on it; plus, of course, the uphill (against gravity) type of situps for the stomach. And a lot of times it's just nice to lie on it with your head downward reversing the flow of the blood to the brain.

Weight-lifting should be accomplished with a barbell, doing mostly lighter weights and repetitions. Again, if you feel you really want to get deeply into this exercise, it's wise to check out a good club or gym in your area, (or one of the many books on the subject). I can give you a few exercises that have worked well for me and for others.

First off, you want to start with a weight that's comfortable to you and won't cause strain. If you're at home, perhaps you'll need a hundred pounds in weights, in addition to your basic barbell. Every person is different, so it's impossible to suggest starting poundage.

1. THE PRESS
This is for building up a good, strong chest, back, and shoulder muscles. Lie on your back, raise the barbell to arms length, and repeat 6 to 10 times. Start with one set, work up to two, and then increase the weight and go back to one set, then two, etc. Probably a five-pound (not more than 10, anyway) increase, each time when you're ready.

2. THE CURL
Try this for the arm muscles. You stand upright, the barbell held (hands facing palms up away from your body) about knee-high, and then you curl the weight up to the chest level. Repeat 6 to 10 times, and work upward in sets, etc. as suggested with the press.

3. DUMBELL SWINGS
This should help in preventing the arms from getting too

weary during your running as you begin to pile up long mileage. With an 8-to-10 pound dumbell, place it on the floor between the legs and beneath the body. Lift it off the floor with one hand, and swing it backwards and forwards between the legs. Then, keeping the arm straight, swing it high over the head and return it to the position (on the floor) between the legs. Do this for about a minute with each arm.

To my way of thinking, these weight exercises are sufficient for the runner. However, some people believe you should also work on strengthening the legs. Again (as in stretching) the hamstrings are important, and if you belong to a club or gymnasium (or spa) they'll have a universal gym machine that can accommodate a hamstring-type of routine. Ask your instructor.

A lot of runners have found yoga to be of benefit in stretching and relaxing. It also helps in posture-development and is a fine mental discipline It's wise, if you're interested in it, to buy a book that pictures and explains the routines—or, better yet, join a yoga class.

Again, I think particular attention should be paid to the abdominal or stomach muscles. The origin of many lower-back problems has been said to be consistent with the weakness of the stomach muscles.

And always remember, your running program is number one. It's what exercises, oxidizes that most important muscle in your body, the heart. And if you have a good training effect (running) program, wherein you're able to work the heart up to 65 per cent of maximum capacity (85 to 90 per cent after my six-month Basic Program), supplementary exercises will be much easier to do and you will benefit more by them.

What is your current level of aerobic fitness? Compare it with others:

Fitness Comparison

Subjects	Country/Area	Men	Women
		(ml/kg/min)	
College freshmen	USA	44	37
Untrained young	USA	43	30
	Canada	49	36
	Scandinavia	59	43
Active young	USA	52	39
	Canada	55	41
	Scandinavia	59	45
Champion distance athletes	World's best	93	75
Untrained (40 to 50 years old)	USA	36	—
	Canada	39	30
	Scandinavia	45	34
Trained (40 to 50 years old)	USA	58	—

Note: U.S. athletes do well in international competition. Fitness scores among untrained groups represent differences in regular daily activity, in a lifestyle that favors the auto over the bicycle.

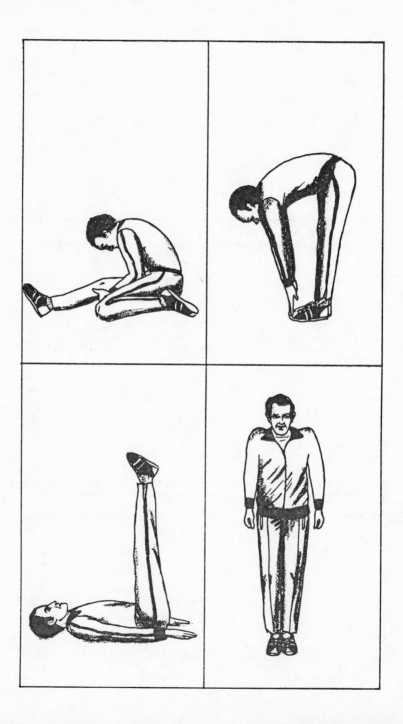

13

PHYSICAL FITNESS

What It Means To You

FITNESS IN AMERICA

Today's American adult generally is concerned about his or
her physical fitness and is reasonably convinced that regular exercise is essential to living a healthy, vigorous life.
This is particularly true of the young, the well educated and
the more affluent members of our society. Most of them believe exercise is "good for you," and they are making some
attempt to get or keep themselves in shape. Except for a
dedicated minority, however, their efforts are too irregular
and too feeble to bring success. Example: of the millions of
adults who jog, one-third do so only once or twice a week,

128

and about the same number jog no more than 10 minutes per outing.

Among Americans past 50 years of age, there is not even general awareness of the human need for physical activity. On the contrary, there appears to be widespread belief that the need for exercise recedes as the years advance, and even that vigorous activity beyond a certain age may be dangerous. Illustration: a sizable majority of men and women past 50 don't exercise at all, but nearly three-fourths of them say they are getting all the exercise they need.

These are highlights of the National Adult Physical Fitness Survey conducted late in 1972 by Opinion Research Corporation of Princeton, N.J., for the President's Council. Here are some more specific findings:

- Forty-five percent of all adult Americans do not engage in physical activity for the purpose of exercise.
- Only 55% of American men and women do any exercise at all, but 57% say they believe they get enough exercise.
- Persons who don't exercise are more inclined to say they get enough exercise than are those who do exercise. Sixty-three percent of the non-exercisers say they get enough exercise, while only 53% of the exercisers believe they are as physically active as they should be.
- Of the 60 million American men and women who engage in various forms of exercise, nearly 44 million walk for exercise. More than 18 million ride bicycles for exercise (as opposed to recreation), 14 million swim for exercise, and 14 million do calisthenics.

WHY FITNESS?

Why do we worry about strength and endurance in a push-button age? These are some of the reasons why exercise and fitness are of value even when the physical demands of living are minimal:

1 - Strength and endurance developed through regular exercise enable you to perform daily tasks with relative ease. You use only a small part of your physical reserve in routine activity.

2 - Skill and agility gained through practice provide for economy of movement. This is another factor in minimizing physical effort required for routine tasks.

3 - Poise and grace are by-products of efficient movement. They help you to feel at ease in social situations and are factors in good appearance.

4 - Good muscle tone and posture can protect you from certain back problems caused by sedentary living.

5 - Controlling your weight is mostly a matter of balancing your food intake with your exercise output. Inactivity is often as critical as overeating in creeping overweight.

6 - To the degree that physical activity helps control your weight, it will also aid in preventing degenerative diseases. Diseases of the heart and blood vessels, diabetes and arthritis strike the obese more often and more seriously than they strike those of desirable weight.

7 - Mounting evidence indicates that exercise is one of the factors in maintaining the health of the heart and blood vessels. Active people have fewer heart attacks and a better recovery rate from such attacks than the inactive.

8 - Enjoyable exercise can provide relief from tension and serves as a safe and natural tranquilizer.

9 - Feeling physically fit helps you to build a desirable self-image. You need to see yourself at your optimum physically as well as in other ways.

10 - Dynamic fitness can help to protect you against accidents and may be a lifesaving factor in emergencies. Reacting quickly and with physical decisiveness may enable you to avert a serious accident.

MORE AWARENESS THAN ACTION

To look your best, to feel your best, and to be able to do your best, you must exercise "regularly." That is man's nature, and modern technology can't change it.

When the activity required of you by your job and other duties falls below the level necessary to support good health, you must supplement it with planned activity. Your sense of well-being, your ability to perform, and even your "survival" depends on it.

You already know that regular, vigorous exercise increases muscle strength and endurance. It also improves the functioning of the lungs, heart and blood vessels; promotes flexibility of the joints; releases mental and physical tensions; and aids in weight control or reduction.

Medical research demonstrates that active persons have fewer heart attacks than sedentary persons. If they do suffer attacks, they recover more readily.

More than half of all lower back pain is due to poor tone and flexibility of the back and abdominal muscles. In many cases, this problem could be prevented or corrected by proper exercise.

In short, exercise can make the difference. The options are mere existence or a full life. The choice is yours.

EXERCISE: HOW MUCH AND HOW OFTEN?

Human beings must exercise regularly to become physically fit. Sufficient rest and sleep, an adequate diet, the absence of excesses, and physical activity are essential to maintaining physical capacities. That is the official position of the American Medical Association. The amount of exercise needed varies from one individual to another, but the AMA recommends 30 to 60 minutes daily as a minimum.

No one can achieve satisfactory levels of strength, endurance and flexibility by working out once a week. More frequent workouts are required to bring about significant changes and both experience and scientific studies show that daily bouts of exercise produce the best results.

The way in which an exercise is done is just as important as how often it is done. For optimum benefit, physical activity must be vigorous enough to give a tonic effect. In other words, the individual must work hard enough to breathe heavily and "break a sweat."

Persons who are unschooled in human physiology, or are unfamiliar with the principles of exercise, seldom work hard enough or long enough to improve circulatory and respiratory performance, or to strengthen muscles. One reason for this is that many of our more popular and enjoyable participatory sports are not taxing enough for fitness purposes. They make a contribution but should be supplemented by an exercise regimen.

Dynamic good health is the objective of a physical fitness program. Performing exercises halfheartedly, or working out briefly and sporadically, cannot move you significantly closer to that goal. Hard work on a regular, sustained basis is the answer.

The level of fitness you can reach depends on your age, your body's built-in potential, and previous conditioning. It also depends on your state of mind. When you want to do something and believe you can, it is much easier to do than it would be otherwise.

When you begin your personal exercise program, you should not expect dramatic overnight changes. But, gradually over the next weeks and months, you will begin to notice a new spring in your step, a new ease in carrying out ordinary daily activities. You will find yourself with more energy left at the end of the working day and a new zest for recreation in the evening. Quite likely, you will be sleeping more soundly than you have for many years and waking more refreshed in the morning. In short, you will be on your way to a better and more complete life.

BEFORE YOU BEGIN

Before beginning any exercise program, it is advisable to

have a medical checkup. If you have not had an examination in the past year, if you are past 40, if you are overweight, or if you have a history of high blood pressure or heart trouble, such an examination may help you to avoid extremely serious consequences.

Chances are your physician will be able to give you an unconditional go-ahead. If not, he may be able to modify the exercises so that they are suited to you.

There are a few persons who, for medical reasons should not undertake any exercise program, unless and until these reasons have been eliminated.

EXERCISE AND WEIGHT CONTROL

Weight control is maintained by keeping energy intake (food) and activity energy output (physical activity) in balance. This is true at all ages for both sexes. When the calories consumed in food equal those used to meet the body's needs, weight will remain about the same. When one eats more than this amount, one will put on fat unless physical activity is increased proportionately.

For years physicians have talked about the varying caloric needs of differing occupations and physical recreations. Yet in their attempts to lose excess fat, weight watchers have often concentrated on counting the calories in their diets and have neglected the role of exercise. For those who are too fat, increasing physical activity can be just as important as decreasing food intake.

Weight depends not only on how many calories are taken in during the day, but also on how many are used up in physical activity. The overly fat person who merely cuts down his intake of food to lose weight will make slow progress since the number of calories needed to maintain the body is much smaller than most people think.

In fact, lack of exercise has been cited as the most important cause of the "creeping" obesity found in modern mechanized societies. Few occupations now require vigorous physical activity. Although there is more time available for recreation, many persons fail to fill this gap by choosing leisure time activities that give them exercise. Even among those who do exercise, their activity is often neither vigorous nor sustained.

Recent studies seem to indicate that lack of physical activity is more often the cause of overweight than is overeating. These studies have compared the food intake and activity patterns of obese persons with those of normal weight. Several age levels—teen-age, adults, and older persons—have been studied. In each instance, the findings showed that the obese people did not consume any more calories than their normal weighted age males, but that they were very much less active.

The person who has a trim figure and wants to keep it should exercise regularly and eat a balanced, nutritious diet which provides sufficient calories to make up for the energy expended. The thin individual who wishes to gain weight should exercise regularly and increase the number of calories he consumes until the desired weight is reached. The overweight person should decrease the food intake and step up the amount of physical activity.

WEIGHT CONTROL FALLACIES

Two basic fallacies have been widely held with respect to exercise and weight control. The first, is that a great deal of time and effort is required to use up enough calories to affect weight materially. The second fallacy is that exercise increases the appetite which will increase, not decrease weight. Scientific experiments on animals and man have demonstrated the falsity of both of these assumptions.

WHAT PHYSICIANS SAY
ABOUT PHYSICAL EXERCISE:

Paul Dudley White, Boston, Massachusetts

"Physical fitness is vital for the optimal function of the brain, for retardation of the onset of serious atherosclerosis which is beginning to appear in early adult life, and for longevity, and a useful and healthy life for our older citizens."

Don B. Chapman, M.D., Houston, Texas

"Daily physical exercise should be maintained throughout the greater portion of one's life. The incidence of cardiovascular disease is greatly reduced in those who keep themselves physically and mentally fit."

J. Roswell Gallagher, M.D., New Haven, Connecticut

"The relationship of regular periods of physical activity to health is clearly established. The AMA Committee on Exercise and Physical Fitness recognizes the preventive, as well as corrective, aspects of exercise and wishes to emphasize the former in regard to the maintenance of health."

Jesse L. Steinfeld, M.D. former Surgeon General, PHS, DHEW, Chevy Chase, Md.

"As a doctor who cares about you as individuals, may I remind you that your own health depends on your decisions and the actions you take on nutrition, smoking, alcohol, and exercise just as much as on what the Nation's health care system provides in the way of medicines, hospitals, and the doctor care."

"If people can be motivated to accept responsibility for their individual health, not only will they have greater vitality and a richer life but medical care will be less costly and more easily available. Preventive medicine, in all its aspects —which include physical activity or exercise, nutrition, smoking, alcohol, and drug abuse programs, etc.,—is usually not the most expensive remedy, but it usually is the most effective."

"Keeping in good physical condition is an individual responsibility. It will make you more effective in your work and at the same time bring personal compensations, one of which is that exercise appears to retard the aging process. As we grow older interest in intense effort appears to decrease, but activity helps maintain capacity for intense effort and thus helps modify some of the effects of aging. The more regular even a modest investment of exercise, the better health you can expect as a return."

Hans Kraus, M.D., New York, N.Y.

"I feel very strongly that vigorous physical exercise for at least one hour daily is essential as a preventive measure for sickness and disability in later life."

Thomas B. Quigley, M.D., Boston, Massachusetts

". . . the principle of a sound mind in a sound body is still the basis of excellence in living."

Theodore G. Klumpp, M.D., New York, N.Y.

"Remaining active is the key to staying alive. Exercise opposes the effects of stroke or heart attack. Blood clots form when the blood flow is sluggish rather than when it is vigorous. Yet many people won't exercise for fear it will provoke a heart attack."

"Others continue to make excuses not to exercise, including: it takes time; it's an interruption in the day's activities; it is often painful. However, the repercussions due to lack of exercise can be more serious. The functions of the body when not used decline, atrophy and finally disappear . . ."

Fred Allman, Jr., M.D., Atlanta, Georgia

"Recent medical research has indicated that degenerative disease and increased mortality are associated with a sedentary life and that physical fitness improves physiological efficiency and results in an increase in endurance, strength, and agility. People who exercise regularly live longer and are less likely to suffer from degenerative diseases."

PRESENT FITNESS

Now, let's try to get some measure of your present fitness. We've put together a simple questionnaire about your general living habits so that you can arrive at your own fitness score.

(1) What is your age? Assign points as follows:

20-25	15
25-30	10
30-35	7
35-40	5
40-45	3
45-50	1
50-up	0

(2) What type of work do you do? Assign points as follows:

Very active	15
Active	10
Semiactive	5
Sedentary	0

Very Active would be for those who are on their feet most of the time, moving about. Generally, the activity is continuous and fairly vigorous.

Active implies a similar situation, but with less movement or less vigorous activity. Busy homemakers, gardening, farming, construction, etc.

Semiactive would still have a person on his feet, but with less moving about. Sales people (in stores), bank tellers, etc.

Sedentary includes those who sit at a desk or at a workbench all day. This, unfortunately, is the lot of most people today.

(3) What kind of recreation do you normally do? Assign points as follows:

Very active	20
Active	10
Semiactive	2
Spectator	0

Very active would mean that you do something of a vigorous nature on a regular basis—up to two or three times a week. This would include sports like tennis, handball, basketball—any activity that gets you pretty worked up.

Active would be much the same, except less regularly, perhaps only once a week or so.

Semiactive is the week-end golfer. Golf, surprisingly

enough, isn't worth too much from a training standpoint, but we will recognize that at least it gets a person on his feet. Also in this category is the occasional tennis player, hand-ball player, etc. He waits so long between games that he's lost all the training effect—but at least he is doing some physical activity.

The *spectator* is just that. He will spend Sunday glued to the TV, and he may even get himself to the stadium for an occasional night game.

(4) How much do you smoke? The best you can do on this question is zero for not smoking at all. Otherwise you can collect only *minus* points which must be deducted from the total (if any!).

Do not smoke	0
½ pack a day or less	-5
½ pack to 1 pack a day	-9
1 pack to 1½ packs a day	-14
More than 1½ packs a day	-20

(5) How much are you overweight? Again hope for a zero score on this one. Other scores will be minus.

0 to 5 pounds	0
5 to 10 pounds	-3
10 to 15 pounds	-6
15 to 20 pounds	-10
20 to 30 pounds	-15
30 to 50 pounds	-20

(6) Are you underweight? The score, if any, is again minus.

0 to 10 pounds	0
10 to 15 pounds	-10

Now get a total score by adding the point values of each question. Find your Fitness Category as follows:

POINTS	CATEGORY	FITNESS
0 or less	I	Terrible
0 to 5	II	Very poor
5 to 12	III	Poor to fair
12 to 25	IV	Fair to good
25 and up	V	Very good

Question 1 shows that the younger a person is the more likely he is to be fit. It takes into account that there is greater resiliency in youth and also that he is not yet so far removed from his school athletics; he has had relatively less time in which to let himself go to seed.

Questions 2 and 3 give points for activity in both work and play. Since play is likely to be more strenuous than work, slightly higher points are awarded to it.

Question 4 again points up the pervasive damage cigarette smoking can have on the health. The system of minus points is interesting in that it shows that nonsmoking is not so much a blessing as smoking is a curse.

Question 5 could be misleading for some individuals. It is possible to be considerably overweight according to the charts, yet the person might be more husky than fat. The best judge of your weight condition is your doctor.

And again we strongly recommend that any program of exercise be preceded by a physical checkup. A score of 20 or 30 does not necessarily mean there isn't some minor problem that might become aggravated by more concentrated exercise.

But, for all its obvious faults, the test, if taken as honestly and objectively as possible, will give a surprisingly accurate appraisal of your general fitness condition.

Aerobic Fitness Prescriptions

Fitness Category	Age	Intensity (in beats/min)	Duration (in calories) Men*	Women*	Frequency	Run Distance (miles)	Run Time (min)	Jog Distance (miles)	Jog Time (min)	Bicycle Distance (miles)	Bicycle Time (min)	Swim Distance (yd)	Swim Time (min)	Walk Distance (miles)	Walk Time (min)
High (over 45 ml/kg/min)	20	164-178	Over 400†	Over 300†	6 days weekly										
	25	162-176													
	30	160-174													
	35	157-171	— Exercise duration and frequency remain the same regardless of age —			3.4+	27+	3.4+	40+	7.8+	47+	1,600+	45+	4.2+	72+
	40	154-168													
	45	151-164													
	50	148-161													
	55	145-158						— Distance and time remain the same regardless of age —							
	60	143-155													
Medium (35-45 ml/kg/min)	20	153-164	200-400	150-300	6 days weekly										
	25	151-162													
	30	148-159													
	35	145-157	— Exercise duration and frequency remain the same regardless of age —			1.7-3.4	14-27	1.7-3.4	20-40	3.9-7.8	24-47	800-1,600	22-45	2.1-4.2	36-72
	40	142-154													
	45	139-151													
	50	136-149													
	55	133-146						— Distance and time remain the same regardless of age —							
	60	130-143													
Low (under 35 ml/kg/min)	20	140-154	100-200	75-150	Every other day										
	25	137-151													
	30	134-148													
	35	130-144	— Exercise duration and frequency remain the same regardless of age —			0.8-1.7	7-14	0.8-1.7	10-20	1.9-3.9	12-24	400-800	11-22	1.0-2.1	18-36
	40	126-140													
	45	122-136													
	50	118-132													
	55	114-128						— Distance and time remain the same regardless of age —							
	60	110-124													

*Caloric expenditure is less for women, because they are smaller than men and burn fewer calories in a given activity.
†For long duration workouts (over 400 calories), training intensity may be reduced to a comfortable level.

14

LONGEVITY AND SEX

The Miracle Training Effect

In my days of running around the world, I've met a lot of "unforgettable characters." But none quite so unforgettable as Larry Lewis. You'll recall that he was the San Francisco hotel waiter who jogged six miles every day in Golden Gate Park—and lived to be 106 years old.

What I liked about Larry was the vigor, and interest in life, that he projected throughout the years. Not only was he working at his job until over age 100, but he used to confide to me—with a twinkle in his eye—that he retained a good amount of sexual energy well into his late, late age.

Of course he was one of a kind. I'm not going to say that if you too, start faithfully running six miles a day, you will be able to get it on like my friend Larry did for so many de-

141

cades. But it certainly is worth a try.

Actually, only recently have researchers started to come up with the overwhelming conclusion: those people who exercise regularly (the cardiovascular kind) have the best chance to not only survive until a ripe old age, but, en route, they'll feel better and have more fun doing it.

Down through the years, most doctors' advice has been to "take it easy." Now, of course, the pendulum is swinging the other way. Literally thousands of doctors are now running and they are advising their patients to do the same.

Dr. Tom Bassler, my pathologist friend mentioned earlier, has done hundreds and hundreds of autopsies. That's his business. He says most deaths are premature. You want to hear his summation of three of civilization's biggest killers: (1) loafer's heart; (2) smoker's lung; and (3) drinker's liver.

It's interesting to me how they go hand-in-hand. Those persons who consistently smoke, and drink, are usually the ones not into exercise of a dedicated and serious nature. But those who are really working on that "loafer's heart" find (if they are smokers and drinkers) that smoking and drinking is not consistent with their new lifestyle and usually give them up.

What's exciting about exercise is that no matter how late in life you start to take it up, you'll benefit by lowering your blood pressure and pulse rate, decrease body fat, and relieve tension—all the while building strength and elasticity into the muscles and arteries.

However, there should be a qualification here. Atherosclerosis (clogged arteries) has been shown to start in some people when they are teenagers, if not before. And so, the earlier you can begin on a regimen of running, the better for your survival. Also, it has been shown that there may be a point (at least for some people) beyond which exercise cannot greatly help them. The earlier in life you start to jog, the greater the possibilities to enjoy the maximum benefits.

STARTING YOUNG

In the chapter on competitive (marathon) running I did not

indicate marathon running for anybody younger than 18 (or 21). But that doesn't mean I'm not in favor of some longer-distance running—or jogging—for children. Even to the extent of an organized program of training. But, also, children should have plenty of leeway for play. You only grow up once.

Prevention Magazine in its February, 1978 issue carried a story about Skippack Elementary School in Pennsylvania, where a fourth "R" has been added to reading, 'riting, and 'rithmetic—it being, of course, running.

In the beginning most students wanted to sprint, but now they are being slowed down so that they will "finish" the half-mile course and start to build in a cardiovascular fitness. Just so that nobody forgets, there's a message on the bulletin board:

—"Jogging is a year-round, every day, lifelong activity."
—"Jogging is a privilege."
—"Being able to use your body is a blessing."

As far as I'm concerned, that reminder should be in every home, in every country throughtout the world.

Unfortunately, studies have found a great many men in their 20s with the bodies of 40-year-olds. And, if they've been into drugs, they're "older" yet. About half the people in the United States probably don't exercise enough—or properly—and approximately 50 million, don't "ever" exercise. Except the hand-to-mouth (feeding) kind.

MASTERS MEETS

People from other countries have for years, organized fitness type, or sport clubs, for all ages. As a result, many have been longer-lived. It was no surprise to me that when David Pain in San Diego, started organizing his Masters (over 40) track meets in the late 1960s, they became an immediate success.

For the most part these "masters" (as old as their 90s) don't run extremely long distances. Instead, they have a complete program (more or less) of track and field events. But they are exceedingly competitive, to the point where often a man in the 50 age category will be running, jumping, throwing superiorly to someone who is competing in the 40s division.

Masters meets are now organized in many communities so you might check around for any in your area. If you don't feel ready to tackle, a mile or two, you might try 100 yards, or other fun events. At the first World Masters competition in Toronto in 1975 some 1,400 came from all continents to compete. One of the meet's highlights was when 90-year-old Duncan MacLean of Scotland beat out 89-year-old Charles Speechley of England in the 100 meter dash. MacLean covered the distance in 22.5 seconds (to the loser's 23.3). I find it fascinating that this same MacLean in his prime in 1904 won the South African 100-yard championship in 9.9 seconds!

SENIOR OLYMPICS

Similarly, Senior Sports International—or the so-named "Senior Olympics" started a few years ago in Los Angeles by an enthusiastic gentlemen named Warren Blaney, has also had very great appeal. It has an "Olympic-type" program that encompasses some 50 activities to include track and field, tennis, swimming, softball, archery, racquet ball, body building, bowling, speed skating, ice hockey, rifle shooting, badminton, beach run, cross-country run, you name it.

This organization has as its creed "Youth Eternal," and Blaney likes to refer to it as a "movement rather than an event." In 1977 there were some 3,000 participants from all over the world. It was at the "Senior Olympics" that 88-year-old Eula Weaver (mentioned earlier) won her medals and holds the "world record" for a mile in her age category.

Indeed, Eula Weaver, has become a symbol of hope to thousands, that the aging process can be slowed down if not completely reversed. The department of gerontology at the University of Southern California has research indicating that people in their 80s have benefited with lower blood pressure and other improvement, after a year's vigorous exercise program. When Eula first started her exercise at 81, she had such poor circulation that she was not able to walk over a hundred feet.

SEXUAL LONGEVITY

One of the first areas that a lack of fitness of either men or women shows up, is in the bedroom. It should be obvious that anything that aids the muscles, heart, lungs, etc. as does running, also sparks the senses. That, in turn, sparks up sexual interest.

I know of and have read about cases of impotence that were cured by the simple act of jogging. Doesn't it make sense to you that you're more of a turn-on to your partner (or any potential partner) if your muscles are firm, the skin tone sparkling, and you have a confident, non-tense demeanor? Plus, if you are a marathon man (or woman) in performance?

I mentioned earlier, that a man's sexual capacity is pretty consistent with his fitness, or physiological age, while a woman's interest and capacity usually keeps on to an older age. That kind of puts the burden on the man, doesn't it, to retain his sexual "youth" for as long as possible?

To me it's really tragic, then, to see 20s-year-olds who are 40s physiologically. By the time that man has reached his late 30s it's practically all over sexually for him (and his companion) for the most part. Happily, the Fitness Institute of Toronto which conducted a study has concluded, "this activity is entirely recoverable thorugh exercise by men between the ages of 35 and 55. There is absolutely no reason why men cannot maintain a vigorous sex life into their 70s." Amen.

KEEPING ACTIVE

When I was growing up in Australia I used to marvel at the Aborigines, who seemed always so fit. Yes, more so than us Aussies, and we're for the most part a healthy, outdoors-type people. I've seen the Aborigines chase down kangeroos for 40 miles, finally wearing them out, and then move in for the kill.

My observation has long since been proved by research. The longest-lived, fittest people (such as the Aborigines, and Hunzas) seem to have long walks (or runs), hard work, and a very basic, natural diet, as the keynotes to their vigor. Today, with the automobile and other transportation so necessary, you have to find other ways than chasing kangeroos or roaming the remote mountain villages if you want longevity. That's why jogging, or, yes, brisk walking, are so important.

The draw-back with walking (as opposed to running) is that it takes so much longer in the matter of time—plus you don't get the heart beating fast enough to get quite the training effect. Tom Bassler says that after a person reaches the level of fitness necessary to make a marathon, he can most likely be protected from arteriosclerosis by doing six miles a day. To walk, it would take nearly an hour and a half per day; a decent jogger cuts the time in half.

However, some people just aren't up to jogging, or running, as they get older—perhaps because the legs pounding on pavement can lead to injuries or there may be heart, back, stomach, or other problems. For these people, the National Jogging Association says that 45 minutes of brisk walking five days a week fulfills its definition of fitness. My own feeling is, better some activity than none.

As a person grows older, he or she can expect to lose a certain amount of speed and agility. And you are slower, also, to round into shape. Plus, seemingly, more susceptible to injuries.

Some people interpret such signs as a time to "do less." Actually, as you grown older, you have to work harder, longer (perhaps) hours to keep in condition. And you have to keep after it consistently.

Just plain old movement, any kind, is the secret if you're beginning a comeback after many years of inactivity. It might take you a year before it all starts to pay off, but your motto should be "Train, Don't Strain!" TDS—remember it.

One of America's top marathoners, Bill Rodgers has said that he first gets in condition to be able to run 26 miles without fatigue—and then he tries to speed it up. You might adopt this "ease of approach" at your level.

THE TRAINING EFFECT

Several times we've mentioned the "training effect," or how the body with its varying important systems responds to the aerobic-type training we're suggesting. Ours will only be a short explanation, but if you want more detail there are plenty of books on the subject.

When you run, what you are doing, in essence, is pumping oxygen (via air) into the lungs, where it is transferred to the blood stream for distribution throughout the body. Obviously, the more air you can process with fit lungs, the better it is for your health.

The same can be said for the volume of blood. Tests show that a fit person has a larger supply of blood than those people of similar size who aren't as conditioned. Exercise—or the training effect—produces more blood (hemoglobin) that is carried to the various parts of the body that are in need of oxygen as an exchange for carbon dioxide and other waste products.

Now, with improved blood flow, the blood vessels or arteries, are opened up and made more pliable, thus lowering the blood pressure—i.e. decreasing the resistance to blood flow. Also, the vessel linings are cleared of materials that could clog. The blood is free to go to the tissues where oxygen is delivered and carbon dioxide carted off.

What pumps all this blood from the lungs throughout the body (and takes carbon dioxide back into the lungs) is that "mini-motor" called the heart. It is a muscle, and it's health depends on it's size and how well the vessels supply it with blood. As a heart that is conditioned gets stronger, it can beat more slowly because it is pumping more blood with each stroke. Thus, resting, an average person might have a pulse rate of 72 beats a minute; a "training effect" conditioned person's rate might be 60, or much lower. Conversely, people in poor condition might beat at 80 (or greater) per minute.

It doesn't take much calculation to determine that in a day's time a person with a pulse rate of 60 puts out 86,400 beats per day. One whose rate is 72 expends 103,680—a difference of almost 20,000. And over a lifetime this is considerable.

What it all means is that the person with a lower heart rate conserves a lot of energy. Plus, there's a protection against strain should the heart suddenly start to beat fast (like that game of tennis or climbing stairs suddenly).

The more you train by continuously and vigorously pumping oxygen into the heart, the stronger you are going to make it, and thus lower the pulse rate. But, of course, the stronger it gets, the more training you have to do in order to get that training effect.

Via the training effect, a heart can also be conditioned to hold near its ultimate rate for a longer time until fatigue sets in, which is precisely what's happening with a superbly conditioned marathon runner who "maximizes" his heart rate for two-plus hours.

You can, of course, apply this same principle in the area of the bedroom, with your partner. Think of all the fun you'll have. Plus, you chances for a longer life span will have increased. And you, too, will have a twinkle in your eye like Larry Lewis, the 106 year old jogger had.

15

RUNNING AND THERAPY

Feeling Good Every Day

Sometimes I feel like the voice of conscience, standing in the background, shaking my head, smiling, and saying "I told you so!"

Many years ago, I "knew" running was a form of mental therapy. It certainly increased my self-image, especially to know that I'm one of the fittest in the world, for my age.

And even if I hadn't accomplished all that I have in competitive races and those ultra long distance city-to-city runs, my overall good health through running would still be my greatest reward. I've seen running change the lives of my best friends and many people who I have helped. I have long felt that running is a way to burn up energy that otherwise might be put into anxiety. I can honestly say that if it hadn't been for my running, I don't know if I'd have made it through a very terrible period in my life while going through a divorce. It was a real blessing to look forward to my running and relief from tension.

Several years ago I had a telephone call from Yakima, Washington. A Mr. Dick Goodman had read about me in Reader's Digest and wanted some advice about stepping up into the special world of the ultra-distance runner. It seems he had concerns about freezing if he trained long distances, when the temperature could drop to 20 degrees-below-zero. I gave him some advice based on my experiences and he felt confident about his ability to handle it.

He then wanted me to work out a training program for him so that he would be able to run 54 miles in celebration of his upcoming 54th birthday. I worked out a special program for him and after six months of slow-long-distance running and spending Saturdays running seven to eight hours in cold weather, he succeeded in achieving his "birthday run."

He recently wrote me, "I think my greatest asset from ultra-distance running is my ability to live as fully and as vitally at age 58 as I did at age 21," he said. "You cannot buy this—it comes only through long command of work which is an outlet and a pleasure to me. The bonus is the great feeling, that of feeling good every day!"

I recently read a comment that most of the better marathoners think about their style—how they're breathing, the way their feet are hitting the ground—while many joggers go through a run thinking about their problems.

PROBLEM SOLVING

I'd say it's true that running is an excellent way to think through, and even solve, problems. An interesting phenomenon, in fact, is now taking place with jogging-running being considered as a possible way to help treat mental patients.

Thaddeus Kostrubala, M.D., a San Diego psychiatrist, has written a book, "The Joy of Running" in which he says, "I have talked to many runners—runners who run long, medium, and short distances—and I have come to the conclusion that running in a particular way is a form of natural psychotheraphy. It stimulates the unconscious and is a powerful catalyst to the individual psyche."

Kostrubala is an avid and pretty good runner himself, and he writes about running with his patients as a departure from the usual in-office, patient-on-coach approach to treatment.

"For as I ran along with my patients, my own unconscious was stimulated. And as we explored the meanings and stimuli for both the patient and therapist, it became quite evident that I could no longer adhere to any stereotyped rules as a therapist. I had to share my inner feelings, or my reticence was immediately perceived by other group members and the entire process would bog down. My only reservations revolved around the concept of confidentiality..."
Kostrubala in his book also notes how his patients changed their life habits. Depressions lifted and even destructive relationships ended.

It could be that Kostrubala is a forerunner of the wave of the future, and a whole new aspect of psychotherapy. The future analyst may take up running as another tool of therapy.

All of these findings are very exciting, as many of these doctors I'm told, are also beginning to use the ancient art of running as a replacement for tranquilizers and other drugs.

Herbert A. DeVries of the University of Southern California's exercise physiology laboratory was quoted in the January, 1978 Runner's World magazine as saying "we found that exercise in single doses works better than tranquilizers as a muscle relaxant among elderly persons with symptoms of anxiety tension—and without undesirable side effects."

THE MENTAL HIGH

Of course, for years I've preached about the "natural high" that awaits if you'll just get out and run. Talk about expanding the mind, Dr. George Sheehan, the New Jersey cardiologist who has written voluminously calls the mental high you can get after a half-hour or so of running a "third wind." He's quoted in "the Complete Jogger," a book by Jack Batten: ". . . For the creative thinker you begin to see analogies between things that are incongruous, which I think is the essense of creativity. You get ideas that you don't get driving a car or sitting at a desk . . . It doesn't always happen, and when it doesn't, running can be a drag . . . (But) the third wind sort of puts you in a different world, a kingdom if you will."

I'm not suggesting the "high" you can get from running as an answer to everything, including sex, although for some its addiction may have reached that proportion. I've known people who claim that they have experienced a sexual turn-on while running in a particular state of excitement.

For most people running, of course, practically guarantees a restful night's sleep. The deeper the better, and if you're really "de-tensed" you'll probably snooze deeply. However, in some cases you may notice a difficulty in getting to sleep or in staying asleep. If that's true you may be overdoing your running to the point of stress and you should cut back.

HEART REHABILITATION

I was dismayed recently to read that the average age of one million Americans who had heart attacks in 1975 was 35, and dropping. Can you imagine that—a heart attack at 35! For me, I was actually reborn at age 40, when I started making my longer runs.

I had a friend in Australia who was a heart specialist. This man would laugh at my running 10 miles a day. In turn, I'd warn him that because he was overweight and inactive, that he was a potential heart attack victim.

Sure enough, he had a serious heart attack at age 38, and fortunately was able to pull through it.

When he got back on his feet, he asked me if I'd give "him" an exercise program. And so I did, and by the end of the year he was up to running six to eight miles a day. But you know what he does now for many of his patients—he gives "them" an exercise program.

In this area of rehabilitation of heart attack patients, I have been especially impressed by the work of Dr. Jack Scaff, Jr. in Honolulu (a real hotbed of jogging!) and Dr. Terence Kavanagh in Toronto.

They are proving that you can take a person with a so-called scarred heart and, slowly but surely (with the proper program of jogging) make the heart strong enough to the point where he (or she) can complete a "marathon." Imagine the turn-about in confidence this gives someone who is very depressed from being practically at the dark end.

But a word to the wise. Jogging certainly has helped a lot of heart attack patients and it is helping to build in others a "protection" against possible attacks. However, only a qualified heart specialist should prescribe a program of physical activity for anyone who has a history of heart trouble, or who has had a heart attack.

Some people have inherited heart trouble, and may even be quite slender and athletic—and unaware of their danger. Even jogging might not be able to help them. In all cases, though, the amount of running (and the type) is important. Remember, I said earlier it's not a good idea to just suddenly go out and start running without a slow-buildup-plan. Also, you should watch out for those sudden-exertion sports unless you are very fit.

These cardiac rehabilitation programs are very carefully conceived, and the patients begin their return to health in many cases with scarcely more than a walk.

So far in this chapter we've talked about the mental therapy and the heart-attack therapy involved in running. But there's also an aspect of the physical injury and discomfort prevention and therapy I'd like to touch on.

BODY CARE

First off, I can't stress enough the importance of the simple (or not so simple) art of massage in the therapy of serious runners, or even joggers. And if you're an ultra-distance runner like me, it's absolutely crucial.

The body has thousands of blood cells and nerve endings around the muscles. When you run, the muscles are being worked so hard that the nutrient-carrying blood can't possibly get there fast enough, and so the result is cramps, and sore, strained muscles.

Massage helps stimulate—to get blood and oxygen into—areas where strain is put on the muscles. And so I suggest massaging the legs for approximately 15 minutes before you go out on a run. And, then, for recuperation, do it again afterwards . . . perhaps in or after a hot bath.

If you don't want a complete hot bath, a hot foot bath could suffice. When I'm on one of my grueling long runs, I take foot baths several times a day. The hot water (filled with Epsom salts) helps the blood to rise to the surface. Followed by a massage, it's great for any problems my feet might be having, or developing.

I'm lucky that both my wife and I have studied massage, and so we know better than most of its values. Of course, if you have someone who's willing to massage you, all the better, because I believe there are currents of energy in our bodies that can be transmitted.

But, if not, a little self-massage can help. Get some dry skin oil and start working yourself from the bottom of your feet up—kneeding, stroking, rolling the muscles (and bones) and moving (and finger-massaging) the joints.

Always remember, of course, that it's mother nature who'll be doing the healing (not you!), but you can be one heck of an assistant. You will be giving nature a greater sense of direction, and your body (via nutrition, sleep, etc.) a greater potential to heal.

A suggestion might be to check out a book on the subject. If you really want to learn about it in depth, you could take a study course at one of the many schools that teach it.

But one tip: it's no trick for the blood to circulate down (you're standing, sitting most of the time). But you want to get it back up, so stroke up TOWARD the heart from your legs. Also, whenever you can, I believe it's best to sit with the legs elevated so that the blood flow is helped upward.

When I'm on the road before bedtime I always get a complete body massage (following that hot bath) to include the back, shoulders, arms, plus legs. And when awakened in the morning the legs are massaged to prepare for the day's running. I've also discovered that frequent stops along the way for treatment of blisters, massage, foot baths, pays off handsomely in the matter of survival. An occasional total-body sponge bath helps.

FEET CARE

Care of the feet is crucial. I rub my feet with rubbing alcohol which is a cleansing and disinfecting agent, but which also hardens (toughens) the skin. Then I brush them with Tincture of Benzoine which helps to toughen the skin and delay those inevitable blisters.

Next, I sprinkle foot powder in the shoes—it absorbs moisture. I rub softened soap around the heel of the shoe—especially the area where the ankle will touch. Then I put a half-inch sponge rubber support at the bottom of the heel inside the shoe. This takes the strain off the knee, ankle, all those other areas of the leg, by helping the foot to hit flat on the ground.

Now, what about blisters? Unless they're just terribly painful you can wait, I'd say, until after your run to treat them. A blister should be drained in a direction away from the blister and quickly disinfected by alcohol. I then use a cream that has both the qualities of being antiseptic and anasthetic, the latter to help the pain.

For strains or bruises that swell I put ice on them, and when the swelling goes down I want the area to be massaged. Putting a very tired and strained knee under an infra-red lamp is often helpful.

Another of my therapeutic techniques is an almost complete fast, one day a week. I believe a total fast is too de-energizing, so I'll eat only fruit—orange, pineapple, etc. and drink water.

So there you have it—a mental and physical look at running. Just remember: "I told you so!"

16

RUNNING CAN CHANGE YOUR LIFE

Developing A New Awareness

"It's the little things that makes jogging such fun—splashing through puddles after a Spring rain, birdsong and wind-song, rabbit tracks in the snow along the road, a muted rose-tinged sunrise, the sweet smell of the awakening earth. It's the chance to think through a problem or let the mind wander back through pleasant memories. It's the feeling of swift freewheeling down a gentle slope or the power of sprinting up over the crest of a hill . . ."

This sensitive writing is from a physician friend of mine, Dr. Robert Caulkins of Delaware, Ohio. Obviously, the good doctor "feels" his jogging as a poet would, and perhaps that is another of the real secrets of running.

Percy Cerutty, one of the world's greatest motivators, used to preach the "wholeness of life"—in other words health and exercise, enjoyment of the arts, love, business activities, and the many other facets of life. His concern was that most people put the cart before the horse. Ambition, making money, comfort, material things, etc. all came first· and then (perhaps) fitness might be squeezed in. He be-'ieved that people had their priorities all mixed up.

Several years ago I came upon a book called "the Ultimate Athlete," written by George Leonard. In it, he talked about "the dance within the game." The reference was to an MS. magazine article in March 1974, entitled "Did O.J. Dance," in which the point was made that most football fans are interested in the final score, or results, while others want to know what really happened in the game, like "Did O.J. Dance?" O.J., of course, being star running back O.J. Simpson.

Leonard's point was, simply, that our culture in its pursuit of results had lost touch with the style, or existance, or movement—in other words the dance—of life. Yes, achievements are important but what was the feeling from the inside during the act of accomplishment? And its "poetry" of movement?

I suppose that's why I was so struck by Dr. Caulkins' "birdsong and windsong" letter to me. Throughout this book I have stressed the development of strength in the legs and an inner power of, primarily, the cardiovascular system. In other words, get the legs in shape (by running) and the rest of the body will follow. Also, how important it is to have the four important internal "machines"—heart, lungs, liver and kidneys—working around the clock in healthy fashion.

But, once you have the so-called "basics" of running fitness and an understanding—which previous chapters have provided—there should be a definition of your goals and objectives.

THE NEW LIFE

Obviously, not everybody gets into running for the same

reason. For some it is, indeed, a cardiovascular fitness and —with the hopes of achieving a "long life." Many want competition with other runners. Others are seeking weight loss. Still others tension-release. For some, group or individual enjoyment. Wives take it up because of husbands, and vice versa; children because of their parents. I know one lady who started running in order to exercise her dog. Another because she was just bored with housework.

Whatever the reason, I think the end result should be a happier life, and how you define it of course depends on your own individual outlook.

James Fixx in "The Complete Book Of Running" concludes that the effects of running are "not extraordinary at all, but quite ordinary." He makes the point that running, stripped to the essense, "keeping our hearts and lungs and muscles fit by constant movement," is experiencing what our ancient counterparts did, 10,000 years ago.

In other words, today's runner can have the best of two worlds: a kind of rugged, individualistic, next-to-nature self, aided by the comforts of modern society. Literally, he can have his cake and eat it, too.

My own feeling is that running helps you to better sort out, or to be discriminating, in what's really important in life. Running gives you the opportunity to be your own person.

Ever since I got into it, first for health, then for the competition and fun, and now still for health and business, running has given my life a focal point. You might say it's my religion, with my body being my church, my temple, and this book my pulpit.

Others, I know, have developed similar feelings. Joe Henderson, a contributing editor to "Runners World," told the Los Angeles Times recently that running is kind of a regulator in my whole life." He added: "Running seems to be my ideal outlet. For me, the immediate psychological benefits of running mean much more than any physical benefits which might come a long time in the future."

It has been well said: ". . . You can get a free ride skiing and a free ride on a skateboard, but you don't get a free ride running. I feel better working for that feeling."

My experience has been that jogging, or running, has kind of a pyramiding effect. One thing builds on another, until you have that "new" person living a changed life.

A MODERN FABLE

I would like to relate my favorite modern-day "fable." Let's take Al, an imaginary potential jogger. He's in his late 30s, overweight, feeling terrible, missing out on most of life —except for all those television shows he watches. He puts in his eight hours at work, drives (buses or takes a train) home to a big dinner, watches the tube and often falls asleep on the couch, or in his favorite chair.

But Al is one of those fortunate people who are sometimes in the right place at the right time. He's shopping at his favorite store and notices this book: "The Official Book Of Running." by Bill Emmerton.

Al picks it up, discovers that Bill Emmerton is an "authority" on the entire subject of running, and buys the book. He can glance through it during the TV commercial breaks.

Somewhere in the process Emmerton convinces Al that he, too, can have a new physique and a marathoner's heart —all he has to do is follow the Basic Program, get out and give it a go.

At first it's slow and sometimes painful, but Al hangs in there. His usual sluggish feeling starts to leave him. Yes, the body is responding, feeling, alive, aware. Friends comment on Al's new sparkle . . . not to mention a smile that's been missing for years.

Al's wife Sally starts to notice, too. Not just because he's home from work now (out jogging) and has dropped 20 unsightly pounds. But a confident, energetic Al is now more aggressive in bed. It's almost as if she were reliving the days years ago when they were first married.

One morning, Al announces that Emmerton suggests fresh fruit, maybe some oatmeal, whole wheat toast for breakfast. How can he be expected to get through a day that's going to include 45 minutes of non-stop running if his body isn't properly nourished?

And, so, not only has Al's general alertness (and efficiency) at work changed, as has his new interest at home, but also his diet. Sally, too, is now eating (and fixing) more natural-food breakfasts, lunches, and dinners.

Since Al is now feeling so aware, he is interested in gaining greater knowledge and exposure. One night he tells his wife that he hasn't time to watch TV and besides, much of it is a bore. Sally almost keels over.

For years trapped in his job, Al decides to look around, to define some new objectives. He hears about an opportunity in his field, applies, has a stimulating interview with the personnel director (who's also a jogger), and is hired.

After Al has finished the Basic Emmerton Program he moves into the advanced. Already he is thinking in terms of the Boston Marathon. Or at least that nearby 10,000 meters race coming up in three weeks.

Because Al is careful, and follows all of Emmerton's safety tips, he progresses without injury. And when race-day arrives he's ready! Of course he doesn't win (he places 51st in a field of 150). But Al is happier than he has been in years, enjoying new experiences, making new friends. He feels alive, in tune with the world and into a much more meaningful life. After just one year at his new job, his boss (also a jogger) informs Al that he has been selected for further advancement in the company. Certainly, this story is a beautiful fable, but if you'll think back it IS entirely possible. "AL," with some variations could be many people reading this book "right now."

My point is simply that the pyramid, or cycle, of jogging-running builds from one step of awareness to the next. From the physical conditioning comes a new mental "excitement." This leads to new inquiries, and knowledge, and acomplishments, and people relations.

RUN FOR FUN

To me, one of the most fascinating things about the entire running experience is that with a few months training, Mr. Average Guy can step up to the starting line at most marathon races (or of lesser distances) and rub shoulders with the Frank Shorters and Bill Rodgers of the world. Actually, this is what physical fitness, and the health of a nation should be about: everybody (well, almost) participates!

Probably the largest segment of runners today are those who claim to "run for fun." They are past the jogging, or pre-conditioning stage (if, that is, they've done their home-work), and they enter races. But winning is not the real goal, as they'd run even if there were no races. They just like the "feel" of running, whether it's "training" or in a race.

So now that you are a newly confirmed "official runner" (having read the Official Book Of Running) I sincerely wish that you will live a happier, healthier, lustier, and longer life. See you at a marathon, or on those Great Jogging Trails that will soon stretch all across the United States and most of the world.

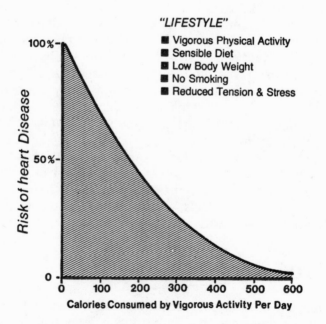

"LIFESTYLE"
■ Vigorous Physical Activity
■ Sensible Diet
■ Low Body Weight
■ No Smoking
■ Reduced Tension & Stress

Risk of heart Disease

Calories Consumed by Vigorous Activity Per Day

Bibliography

Ald, Roy. *Jogging, Aerobics and Diet.* New York:
New American Library, 1968.

Arnot, Phil and Elvira Monroe. *Run for Your Life.* San Carlos,
Calif: Wide World, Inc., 1977.

Batten, Jack. *The Complete Jogger.* New York:
Harcourt, Brace Jovanovich, 1977.

Bowerman, William J. and W.E. Harris. *Jogging.* New York:
Grosset & Dunlap, 1967.

Burger, Robert E., *Jogger's Catalog,* M. Evans & Co., 1978.

Bush, Jim. *Inside Track.* Chicago: Henry Regnery Company,
1974.

Cooper, Kenneth H. *Aerobics.* New York: Bantam Books,
1968.

_____. *The New Aerobics.* New York: Bantam Books, 1970.

Fisher, A. Garth and Clayne R. Jensen. *Scientific Basis of
Athletic Conditioning.* Philadelphia: Lea & Febiger, 1972.

Fixx, James F. *The Complete Book of Running.* New York:
Random House, 1977.

Frederick, E.C. *The Running Body.* Mountain View, Calif.:
World Publications, 1973.

Glover, Bob & Shepard, Jack. *Runner's Handbook,* Penquin
Books, 1977.

Henderson, Joe. *Jog, Run, Race*. Mountain View, Calif.: World Publications, 1977.

Kostrubala, Thaddeus. *The Joy of Running*. Philadelphia: J.B. Lippincott, 1976.

Percival, Jan, Lloyd Percival and Joe Taylor. *The Complete Guide to Total Fitness*. Scarborough, Ontario: Prentice-Hall of Canada, 1977.

Runner's World Magazine. *The Complete Runner*. Mountain View, Calif.: World Publications, 1974.

_____. *The Runner's Diet*. Mountain View, Calif.: World Publications, 1972.

_____. *Running Psychology*. Mountain View, Calif.: World Publications, 1972.

_____. *Running with Style*. Mountain View, Calif.: World Publications, 1975.

_____. *Running with the Elements*. Mountain View, Calif.: World Publications, 1974.

Sheehan, George A. *Dr. Sheehan on Running*. Mountain View, Calif.: World Publications, 1975.

Sheehan, George A. Dr., *Running & Being*. Simon and Schuster, 1978.

Smith, Nathan J. *Food for Sport*. Palo Alto, Calif.: Bull Publishing Company, 1976.

Ullyot, Joan. *Women's Running*. Mountain View, Calif.: World Publications, 1976.

Van Aaken, Ernst. *The Van Aaken Method*. Mountain View, Calif.: World Publications, 1976.